NO FEAR ALGEBRA

Titles in the **NO FEAR** Skills Series

Algebra

Grammar

Math

Spanish

Vocabulary

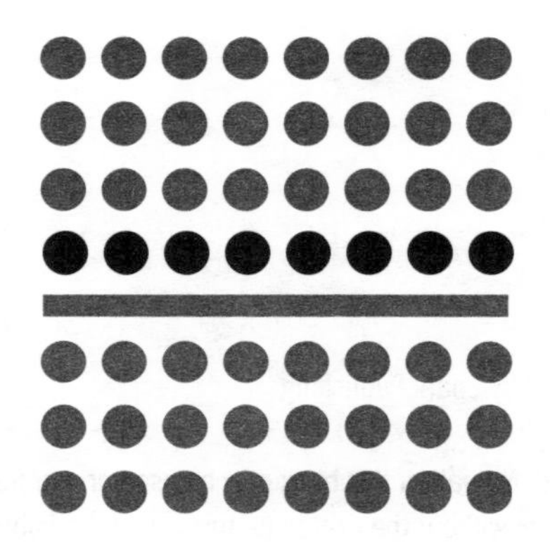

NO FEAR ALGEBRA

SPARK PUBLISHING

Spark Publishing
A Division of Barnes & Noble Publishing
120 Fifth Avenue
New York, NY 10011
www.sparknotes.com

ISBN-13: 978-1-4114-0133-4
ISBN-10: 1-4114-0133-6

Please submit changes or report errors to *www.sparknotes.com/errors*

Written by Kathy Furgang

Printed and bound in Canada

CONTENTS

INTRODUCTION.......................... VIII
It's Not a Problem.......................... viii

CHAPTER 1: THE BASICS: MEET LETTER X......3
What Is Algebra?.......................... 3
Variables.......................... 4
Expressions.......................... 4
Translating Algebra into English.......................... 5
Translating English into Algebra.......................... 5
Avoiding Confusion.......................... 6
YOUR TURN.......................... 7

CHAPTER 2: POSITIVE & NEGATIVE NUMBERS.......................... 9
Signed Numbers.......................... 10
YOUR TURN.......................... 14

CHAPTER 3: SIMPLIFYING EXPRESSIONS..... 17
Parentheses.......................... 18
Brackets and Braces.......................... 18
Distributive Property.......................... 19
Combining "Like" Terms.......................... 20
Working from the Inside Out.......................... 21
Polynomials, Etc... 21
YOUR TURN.......................... 23

CHAPTER 4: SOLVING EQUATIONS......... 25
Equations.......................... 26
First-Degree Equations.......................... 26
Isolating the Variable.......................... 27
YOUR TURN.......................... 30

CHAPTER 5: EQUATIONS WITH FRACTIONS . . 33
Fractions . . . 34
Variable in the Denominator . . . 35
Cross Multiply . . . 37
YOUR TURN . . . 38

CHAPTER 6: TWO-VARIABLE EQUATIONS . . . 41
X and Y in the Same Boat . . . 42
Finding X and Y . . . 42
Selecting a Value for X . . . 43
Ordered Pairs . . . 44
YOUR TURN . . . 46

CHAPTER 7: EXPONENTS . . . 49
Exponent Basics . . . 50
Operations with Exponents . . . 50
Order of Operations . . . 51
Roots . . . 52
Simplifying Roots . . . 53
YOUR TURN . . . 55

CHAPTER 8: THE LAWS OF EXPONENTS . . . 57
Exponent Laws . . . 58
Multiplication Law . . . 58
Power of a Power Law . . . 59
Power of a Product Law . . . 60
Power of a Fraction Law . . . 60
Division Law . . . 61
Mixing It Up . . . 61
YOUR TURN . . . 63

CHAPTER 9: MULTIPLYING POLYNOMIALS . . 65
Gearing Up . . . 66
Multiplying Binomials . . . 66
FOIL Method . . . 66

Squaring a Binomial 67
Multiplying Polynomials 68
YOUR TURN 69

CHAPTER 10: WORD PROBLEMS 71
Problems with a Variable 72
Word Problem Cheat Sheet 73
Word Problems with Linear Equations 74
Word Problems with Two Unknowns 75
YOUR TURN 77

CHAPTER 11: GRAPHING COORDINATES 79
Graph Basics 80
Ordered Pairs 81
Negative Coordinates 82
Lettered Coordinates 83
YOUR TURN 84

CHAPTER 12: LINEAR EQUATIONS 87
Linear Equations 88
Solving for Two Variables 88
More Possibilities 89
Plotting the Coordinates 91
Intercept 91
YOUR TURN 93

CHAPTER 13: TIPS 95
Checking Your Answers 96
Showing Your Work 96
Practice, Practice, Practice 97
A Final Farewell 97
YOUR TURN 99

ANSWER KEY 101

INTRODUCTION

IT'S NOT A PROBLEM

Okay, I know you're probably not too interested in math. Very few of us are. Even the word *algebra* might give you a little bit of a sweaty-palm feeling, right? But, unfortunately, just because you don't like math doesn't mean you get to skip it for the rest of your life. I mean, you still have to take math classes and need to get good grades. Well, that's exactly why you need *No Fear Algebra*.

I know how quickly things can get confusing when numbers are involved, so I've explained everything as plainly as humanly possible. You can use this book by reading from cover to cover, or you can look up key topics you're having trouble with and shoot straight to that section. Whatever works for you is fine.

People sometimes freak out when they see the word *algebra*. Or when they see the letter *x*. I'm here to say, "Nah, it's not a problem."

Anyway, read the book. Learn about me. Get to know the ups and downs of my strange high school experience. Most of all, pick up a thing or two about algebra. You won't be sorry, and your report card will thank you.

NO FEAR
ALGEBRA

CHAPTER 1
THE BASICS: MEET LETTER X

YESTERDAY

Okay, I know you're probably not too interested in math. But no worries—I'm here to help. I suppose I should introduce myself. I'm Ryan Hall, algebra tutor *extraordinaire*. Yes, get a life, I know. I've been talking to you for all of two seconds and you probably have me pretty much figured out: All I know is algebra. I literally *have no life*. But this is not entirely my fault. You see, I was in this skateboarding accident, and I hit my head, and now I have no ability to form new memories. I can remember everything that happened before my accident, but my short-term memory is completely gone. Stop me if I've explained this to you already. I don't remember seeing you before in my life, but even if I had met you, I wouldn't remember.

I bet the mere mention of algebra is enough to give you a bit of a sweaty-palm feeling, right? I'm here to tell you, "Nah, it's not a problem."

WHAT IS ALGEBRA?

When you get right down to it, **algebra** is finding an unknown number in a problem. That's it. The unknown number is referred to by a letter, such as an x.

What do I mean by an unknown number? For instance, you know that $2 + 1 = 3$. But what if you took out the 1 and put in an x? Suddenly, you've got $2 + x = 3$. Now you're doing algebra! The x is an unknown number.

Of course, most problems are more difficult than that, but right now we're just talking about the concept, okay? When you do algebra, you want to know what number to put in place of that x in order to solve the problem.

VARIABLES

Before we get too far, let's get some vocabulary out of the way. I'll bet you didn't think there would be vocabulary to learn in an algebra class. Don't worry, there's not too much.

Probably the most important word to know is **variable**. That's the name math folks give that unknown number we were just talking about. That's the letter x in the problem we looked at above. It's called the variable. In this problem:

$$4 + x = 12$$

x is the variable. It could also be a y ($4 + y = 12$), or it could be an n ($4 + n = 12$). In all three cases, the answer, 8, is represented by a variable: x, y, n. Get it? It's any letter that represents a number.

But a variable has no fixed number value. It changes from problem to problem. That's right: it *varies*. Like, suppose we change the 12 in this example to 20:

$$4 + x = 20$$

Now the value of x (or y, or n) changes to 16.

EXPRESSIONS

Just a couple more vocabulary words and we'll be free and clear. In algebra, an **expression** is a group of letters and numbers together, connected with symbols such as a plus or minus sign. Here is an example of an expression in algebra:

$$4x + 10$$

You can break up an expression into smaller parts. The 10 and the $4x$ are both called **terms**. They are individual parts of an expression. The 4 in this example is called the **coefficient**. A coefficient is a number multiplied with a variable.

$$\overbrace{4x + 10}^{\text{expression}}$$

variable

coefficient

TRANSLATING ALGEBRA INTO ENGLISH

One problem people have when they do algebra is that they see all these numbers and they freak out. But algebra can be expressed in plain English. Watch:

$$3x - 7$$

This means "3 times a number minus 7." Here's another one:

$$8 + 5x$$

This can be translated into plain English by saying "8 plus 5 times a number."

TRANSLATING ENGLISH INTO ALGEBRA

You probably never thought you would have to, but you can also translate English into algebraic expressions. Use x whenever you're talking about "a number." So, when you say, "a number minus 4," you are saying,

$$x - 4$$

The point of this is not for you to run out and write algebra problems. The point is for you to understand that you can make sense out of an algebraic expression and not be intimidated by it. We'll get into how to solve the expressions, but you have to start with understanding what the expression means.

Sometimes, you need to deal with two different variables in the same expression. They must be stated as two different letters. So, when you say, "12 plus a number minus another number," you express it as

$$12 + x - y$$

AVOIDING CONFUSION

Here's an interesting problem with algebra:

$$17 \times x$$

The multiplication sign looks an awful lot like the variable, doesn't it? People thought there ought to be a way to avoid this confusion. There are three different ways you can write that same expression without confusion.

$$17 \cdot x$$
$$17x$$
$$17(x)$$

Each means the same thing: "17 times a number." The symbols are all used to express multiplication.

CLASSICAL ALGEBRA

How long have people been suffering through algebra classes? Well, that's pretty hard to say, but algebra itself has been around for more than 4,000 years. That's a lot of equations! It all started back in ancient Egypt and Babylon when people started solving problems for an unknown variable, just like you just did. Things took off from there, algebra spread around the world, and now here we are.

YOUR TURN

1. Which is the *variable*?

   $7y - 11$

2. Is this a *term* or an *expression*?

   $8 + 14 - x$

3. Which is the *coefficient*?

   $19n \cdot y$

Write these expressions:

4. 12 times a number
5. A number plus another number
6. 9 plus a number times 8
7. 8 times a number minus that same number
8. A number minus 1 plus another number
9. 3 times a number plus 5 times another number
10. 450 times 11 plus 2 times a number

Write what these expressions mean in English:

11. $4y + 0$

12. $81 \cdot x - y$

13. $2x + 3y$

14. $7 + y$

15. $12n - 3c$

2

CHAPTER 2
POSITIVE AND NEGATIVE NUMBERS

TWO DAYS AGO

Now, I know you're probably not too interested in math. Very few of us are. But just because you don't like math doesn't mean you get to skip it for the rest of your life. I suppose I should introduce myself. My name is Ryan Hall, and I'm here to help. One thing you should know about me: I injured my head in an accident, and now I can't make new memories. I don't remember yesterday or the day before any more than if they were tomorrow.

Please excuse me if I seem a little tense today. I'm about to give a tutoring session to this guy named Craig—the star player of the basketball team. Don't get me wrong. I love the people I tutor—I practically live for them. But Craig's a big shot, you know? Big man on campus. I bet he thinks that just because he doesn't like math, he gets to skip it for the rest of his life. Well, I've got news for him.

But that's not why I'm nervous. What's making me feel weird is that I actually used to be friends with Craig back in sixth grade. We used to spend hours in his driveway, doing ollies and kick flips on our skateboards all afternoon, until his mother would call us in for some chocolate chip cookies and milk. His mother—don't get me started on *her*. But all that was a long time ago—I haven't talked to Craig since we were little kids. At least, I don't think I have.

Just seeing Craig's driveway is enough to send me flying down memory lane. And what have we here? I might have known. There in the driveway, his back still turned to me, is Craig. On his skateboard. He looks *exactly* the same—same baggy jeans, same Stussy hooded sweatshirt. He's about to do a kick flip. A devilish impulse comes over me. I creep up behind him and knock him off his board as he's doing the flip.

"Yo, Craig! How *are* you, dog? How you been?"

He starts to cry.

And then I realize: if this were really Craig Gurevich, *he would have grown up too.*

Whoa. Okay, so I just knocked over an innocent sixth-grader. Not Craig. Sometimes I get a bit confused about things, I admit. But *algebra*? No worries there. I'm here to help.

SIGNED NUMBERS

Remember number lines? A **number line** is a line that represents numbers in a sequence. The most interesting thing about number lines is that they continue forever in both directions. So, when you have a 0 on a number line, you have positive numbers on the right side and negative numbers counting down on the left.

$$-3 \quad -2 \quad -1 \quad 0 \quad 1 \quad 2 \quad 3$$

A **signed number** is a number with a plus or a minus sign in front of it. You usually won't see a plus sign to indicate a positive number, such as +3. When the number is written as just 3, it's understood that it's a positive number.

But for a negative number, we have to indicate that it's negative with a minus sign, such as -45.

ABSOLUTE VALUE

Whether you're talking about +37 or -37, you're still talking about 37 units of something, right? Whether it's 37 units to the right on the number line or 37 units to the left on the number line, the value of the number is still 37.

That's why the number that remains when you remove a sign from a number is called the **absolute value** of the number. The symbol | | is used to indicate absolute value. The absolute value of -10 is 10, and it's written as

$$|-10| = 10$$

Remember, the absolute value of a number is always a positive number. It's the number without a sign in front of it.

One word of advice about signed numbers. They're very important in algebra. A negative sign is often a minus sign, a positive sign is often an addition symbol, and signs change so often in algebra from positive to negative and back again that your head will spin if you're not ready for it. So here we go.

ADDING SIGNED NUMBERS

To add two signed numbers together, first take a look at the signs. If they're both the same sign, add the numbers together (the absolute value of the numbers) and then just tack on the sign when you're finished. In effect you're just counting backward on the number line. Like this:

$$(-9) + (-13) = -22$$

Notice that we put the negative numbers in parentheses so the plus and minus signs aren't confusing to read when we do operations. It makes sense, and it makes things clearer.

Now let's look at an example of adding two numbers with different signs:

$$8 + (-15)$$

Since one of the signs is negative, you subtract the smaller absolute value from the larger one. Then tack on the sign that belongs to the larger absolute value:

$$15 - 8 = 7$$

The answer becomes a negative number because it takes on the sign of the 15, which is negative:

$$8 + (-15) = -7$$

SUBTRACTING SIGNED NUMBERS

To subtract signed numbers, add the opposite of the sign. Let's take a look at an example:

$$8 - (-2)$$

The opposite of -2 is 2. So, 8 + 2 = 10.

$$8 - (-2) = 10$$

Now try (-3) - (-5). The opposite of -5 is 5. So, -3 + 5 = 2. To do the subtraction problem, you have to remember how to do the addition problem. Subtract the absolute value of 3 from 5, and keep the sign positive because the sign on the 5 is positive.

MULTIPLYING SIGNED NUMBERS

To multiply two signed numbers, multiply the absolute values of the numbers. If the signs are the same, it is positive. If the signs are not the same, make the answer negative. For example,

$$3(-11) = -33$$

First, multiply: 3 times 11 is 33. Then tack on the negative sign. If the signs are different, the answer is negative.

What if the signs are the same?

$$(-5)(-2) = 10$$

Multiply: 5 times 2 is 10. Since the signs are both negative, the answer is positive. If you are multiplying two numbers with the same sign, whether they've both negative or both positive, the answer will be positive.

DIVIDING SIGNED NUMBERS

Dividing two signed numbers is a lot like multiplying them. Divide the absolute values for the numbers. If the signs are not the same, make the answer negative:

$$120 \div (-3) = -40$$

If the signs are the same, make the answer positive:

$$-35 \div (-7) = 5$$

THE FATHER OF ALGEBRA

A Greek mathematician named Diaphanous, who lived around 250 BCE, is thought to be the first person to write down ways to express algebraic equations and solutions. While algebra had technically been around for about 3,000 years before Diaphanous, he was known as the first person to write this stuff down. He wrote a famous work called *Arithmetica*, which contains more than 150 algebra equations and solutions. But he didn't use the rules we use today for solving problems. In fact, he solved all his problems with different methods! And here's another kicker. He didn't use symbols, so every problem was expressed in words.

YOUR TURN

1. Find $| -2 |$

2. Find $| 0 |$

3. Find $| +7 |$

4. Write the absolute value of -142 as an algebraic term.

5. Find $| -40 |$

Solve the following expressions:

6. $-8 + 4$

7. $14 + (-6)$

8. $(-5) - (-2)$

9. $(-8) - (+7)$

10. $(+40) - (-30)$

11. $-8(-4)$

12. $(-14)(-3)$

13. $(-5)(+9)$

14. $(-11)(15)$

15. $-12 \div 2$

16. $-20 \div -4$

17. $(-8) + (-9)$

18. $(-14) + (3)$

19. $5 - (17)$

20. $(-4)(+10)$

3

CHAPTER 3
SIMPLIFYING ALGEBRAIC EXPRESSIONS

THREE DAYS AGO

Before I teach you how to simplify algebraic expressions, I should mention that since my accident, I can't form new memories at all. I don't remember whether I've met you before or what we talked about yesterday.

My name's Ryan Hall, by the way. I apologize if I seem a little tense today. I'm on my way to teach simplifying expressions to this basketball player named Craig. I'm meeting him at his house, and I haven't been there since sixth grade, when I embarrassed myself outrageously with his mom in this horrible scene that I'd rather not relive right now. Let's just say that I opened the wrong door and caught his mom in an embarrassing situation. So, I'm a little nervous.

Craig lets me in, and as I enter his house, I see that everything looks just as it did when we were in sixth grade—indeed, just as it did that fateful day as I fled down those stairs and out the door burning with shame and anguish.

But before I get too deep into nostalgia, who should enter the room but Craig's mother! She's smartly dressed in a white silk blouse with matching long, white silk scarf, her lustrous brown hair gathered back into a high ponytail, her pert little nose wrinkling as she smiles at us over the silver tray she's holding.

"How nice to see you, Ryan. I brought you boys some milk and cookies."

"Um, no thanks. They look great, but for some reason, I feel really full, Mrs. G."

"That's fine, Ryan."

What is wrong with me! The smile is gone. Does she think I was rude? Why didn't you take the cookie, you idiot! Say something—save the moment—say anything!

"Uh, Mrs. G., you haven't changed at all. You're just as beautiful as you were when I used to come here."

Argh. Some days, it's just easier to think about algebra. Got that sweaty-palm feeling yet? I'm here to tell you, "Nah, it's not a problem."

PARENTHESES

Have you ever done math problems with parentheses? Maybe you've heard the mnemonic device for the **order of operations**. It goes Please Excuse My Dear Aunt Sally. That stands for Parentheses, Exponents, Multiplication, Division, and Subtraction. This tells you that you should work on expressions that are inside the parentheses first.

So, for example, when you see a problem like this, you know you should work on the terms in the parentheses first.

$$3 + 4 - (9 + x)$$

BRACKETS AND BRACES

The parenthesis is not the only grouping symbol in the math world. Sometimes in algebra you'll find symbols called **brackets**. They look like this:

$$[\ ]$$

And sometimes you'll find grouping symbols called **braces**. They look like this:

$$\{\ \}$$

The symbols separate different sets of expressions. They can also be used along with parentheses in the same expressions. This allows you to have a long string of terms, with brackets inside parentheses inside braces. Don't worry. You'll see how all of this stuff looks when we get into solving equations. For now, it's just a heads-up. The symbols are meant to help, not to make things look more confusing.

DISTRIBUTIVE PROPERTY

When you see expressions that are grouped, your first job is to ungroup them, or get rid of the parentheses. There's a little rule to help you do that. The rule is called the **distributive property**, and it says

$$a(b+c) = ab+ac$$

See how the *a* was "distributed" evenly to each letter across the parentheses? The *a* is a coefficient in this example. The *a* gets multiplied with each letter across the parentheses.

Let's try using the distributive property with a real problem:

$$7(x+3)$$

Look! It's our first algebra problem with a variable! Call in the media. We're on our way. Let's distribute the 7 across the problem by multiplying it with each term:

$$7x+7(3)$$

Okay, now take that one step further and do any other multiplication you can. We can't do $7x$ because we don't know what number x represents. But we can finish up the 7(3):

$$7x+21$$

The distributive property works the same way with subtraction. The rule is

$$a(b-c) = ab-ac$$

COMBINING "LIKE" TERMS

Now that you know how to remove grouping symbols by using the distributive property, you can work on longer problems. Just keep working through the line, one grouping at a time, from left to right:

$$3(x-1)-4(2-1x)-(x+1)$$

The minus signs between each term should be combined with the coefficients and treated as signed numbers. So, use your knowledge of signed numbers to work through each term. Notice that with the last grouping of numbers, you're distributing the negative sign across the parentheses. This changes the signs within the group, so the next step looks like this:

$$3x-3-8+4x-x-1$$

As you can see, when you use the distributive property, you are left with some terms that have variables and some that don't. You want to combine all of the "like" terms. That means you should group all of the variables together and all of the coefficients together. Your knowledge of signed numbers will help you here too:

$$(3x+4x-x)-3-8-1$$

With each step, you are combining another term. Keep going until the expression has just one variable, one coefficient, and one integer.

$$6x-12$$

WORKING FROM THE INSIDE OUT

When you have a long expression with several grouping symbols, such as brackets and parentheses, work from the inside out. First, solve the smaller groups inside the large grouping symbol. Let's take a look at how that works:

$3\{x - 2[5 - (x + 1)] + 1 - 2\}$	Get rid of inside parentheses.
$3\{x - 2[5 - x - 1] + 1 - 2\}$	Then get rid of brackets.
$3\{x - 10 + 2x + 2 + 1 - 2\}$	Distribute the 3 across.
$3x - 30 + 6x + 6 + 3 - 6$	Combine the like terms.
$9x - 27$	

POLYNOMIALS, ETC.

Here's another word about vocabulary. Sometimes, you'll run across big, fancy words that mean simple, little things. *Polynomials, binomials, trinomials* . . . – these are all fancy words for the number of terms in an expression. Remember, terms are separated from other terms with a plus or minus sign.

A **binomial** is an expression with exactly two terms.

$3(4 + 2x) + 11$ binomial

A **polynomial** has more than two terms.

$5x + 6(2x) - 17 + (3 \cdot 4x)$ polynomial

A **trinomial** has exactly three terms.

$10y + 7y + 8$ trinomial (also a polynomial)

BRACES OR BRACKETS?

What's the difference between parentheses, braces, and brackets? When should you use them? Well, there's really no difference at all except in the way they look. Just imagine a long equation with grouping symbols inside grouping symbols—and suppose only parentheses were used? It would look so confusing, you wouldn't know which group went with which parentheses. Adding brackets and braces makes it easier to tell groups apart. The order goes like this: { [( )] }. Parentheses are the most commonly used grouping symbol. Brackets are used to enclose a group with parentheses inside it. Braces enclose brackets and are the least used of the grouping symbols.

YOUR TURN

Use the distributive property to simplify these expressions.

1. $14(x + y)$

2. $5(x - 4) + 4(3x + 7)$

3. $x - [7 - 2(x + 1)]$

4. $5(7x - 3 + x) - (x + 5)$

5. $-3(4 + x) - 5[x - (3 - x)]$

6. $y(8 + 2) + x(4 - 1)$

7. $3y(4 - 2y) - 2[y + (3x + 2x)]$

8. $2\{y - 3(6 - [2 + y]) + 3\} - 2$

9. $4 + 2(x - 2[5 + x])$

10. $14(2x + 3x) - x(5 - 4x)$

SIMPLIFYING EXPRESSIONS

CHAPTER 4
SOLVING EQUATIONS

FOUR DAYS AGO

Hello! I'm Ryan, algebra tutor *extraordinaire*. Yes, get a life, I know. But listen—just because you don't like math doesn't mean you get to skip it for the rest of your life. I'm here to help.

One thing you should know about me is that I have no short-term memory. I can't form new memories at all. I remember everything up to my accident, but since then, it's a blank. But don't worry—I'm a whiz at this algebra stuff.

I admit I'm a little nervous today because I'm going to this guy Craig's house to tutor him for the first time. He and I used to be friends, but that was ages ago, when we were kids. I haven't been there since I embarrassed myself horribly in front of his mother back in sixth grade. I'm sure she's forgiven me, but I know she couldn't have forgotten, so I feel a bit awkward. My palms are a bit sweaty, to tell you the truth.

Just walking to Craig's house is enough to send me flying down memory lane. I turn into his driveway and am hit with a hundred flashbacks of the two of us skateboarding there and nearly breaking our necks daring each other to do stupid tricks. He was always more athletic than I was, but I wasn't too bad on a skateboard. Until my accident, of course.

Anyway, after Craig lets me in, it isn't long before I have to confront my worst fear. In from the kitchen, carrying a silver tray of milk and cookies, walks his mom. She's dressed from head to toe in winter white—a pashmina with a fringe and a long, tailored skirt with a slit up the side—and her lustrous brown hair is gathered up into a French twist.

"How nice to see you, Ryan. I brought you boys some milk and cookies."

I reach out to take a cookie. I want to take it. I really do. But somehow, the thought makes me slightly queasy. Why do I feel so full? *Disgustingly* full. "Er, no thanks, Mrs. G."

Idiot! Say something. Say something. Rescue the moment before she goes away.

"Um, Mrs. G.?" My voice cracks. "You look just as beautiful as you did when

I was a kid."

"Poor Ryan. You never change, do you?"

I can't remember if I change or not—I'd rather just think about algebra. Does the mere thought, the merest hint, of the word *algebra* make your skin crawl, your palms itch, and your breath come in short, ragged gasps? I bet it does. But I'm here to tell you, "Nah. It's not a problem."

EQUATIONS

Have you noticed that up until now we haven't been working with an equal sign in any of our problems? That's not a coincidence. I did that on purpose. We've been working only with expressions so far. Now we're going to start working with equations. An equation is made up of two expressions that are equal. In other words, there's an expression, an equal sign, and another expression on the other side of it. Here's an example:

$$5(x-1) = 24$$

Let's learn how to deal with the left and the right side of the equal sign at the same time.

FIRST-DEGREE EQUATIONS

In this chapter, we solve only first-degree equations. Here's what a first-degree equation is:

1. There's only one variable.
2. There are no exponents in the problem.
3. The variable is not in the denominator of a fraction.
4. The equation uses more than one operation.

This will keep things fairly simple for now until we feel comfortable doing what needs to be done to solve an equation and finally figure out what that pesky x equals.

ISOLATING THE VARIABLE

In order to solve an equation in algebra, you have to simplify the expressions as best as you can and then move some things around. What you are trying to do is put the x all by itself on one side of the equation. That means that by the end of your problem, you'll end up with something that looks something like this:

$$x = 14$$

Remember, this is our end goal. It's called isolating the variable. There's a four-step plan for doing this that you can take with you forever. It's the basis for solving any algebra problem. Let's take one example problem and go through our four-step plan for solving equations. The first step is to *simplify*. Here we go.

STEP 1: SIMPLIFYING

You already know how to do this by using the distributive property and combining like terms. This time, you do it for both sides of the equation. Here's our example:

$$2[3 + x + 4(2x - 1)] = 8 - x + 3$$

Work slowly and carefully, following the **order of operations**. That means that you work on parentheses first. If you see more than one kind of grouping symbol, solve for the innermost group first and work your way out. Luckily, on this equation, the right side of the equal sign doesn't need much simplifying, so let's concentrate on the left side:

Simplify the innermost group.	$2[3 + x + 8x - 4] = 8 - x + 3$
Distribute the 2.	$6 + 2x + 16x - 8 = 8 - x + 3$
Combine like terms.	$-2 + 18x = 11 - x$

This is as far as you can go on each side of the equal sign because you've combined the like terms. All of the coefficients and variables are together, and all of the like terms are together. Step 1 is complete.

STEP 2: TRANSPOSING

Our next step is to **transpose**, or move, terms from one side of the equation to the other. You want to put all of the variables with their coefficients on one side of the equation and all of the terms without variables on the other side of the equation.

This transposing stuff works because you're really adding a 2 to both sides of the equation. When you do the same thing to both sides of the equation, everything stays equal, and that's what we want to do. So, on the left side of the equation, the 2 goes away because -2 plus 2 is 0. On the right side of the equation, you have your integers grouped together like you wanted. Both sides of the equation are treated equally, so everyone's happy.

You don't have to write this step out, because it gets a bit confusing. But there's one important thing to know when you transpose. You have to change the sign when you move something from one side of the equal sign to another. For example, if you have a positive number on the left expression and you want to move it to the right, you have to make it a negative number. Once it jumps over that equal sign, it becomes the opposite of itself.

Here's where we last left our problem:

$$-2 + 18x = 11 - x$$

Now, let's transpose.

Move -2 to the right side, change signs.	$18x = 11 - x + 2$
Move $-x$ to the left side, change signs.	$18x + x = 11 + 2$

STEP 3: SIMPLIFYING AGAIN

Now that we've got all of the variables on one side of the equation, we can simplify again. Combine terms on both sides of the equation. When you're working with one side of the equation, don't forget that you have to do the same type of thing to the other side of the equation. So, if you're simplifying the coefficients on the left, simplify the terms on the right as well. You can do it in two steps to be clearer, but don't forget!

Here's where we left off:

	$18x + x = 11 + 2$
Combine like terms on the left.	$19x = 11 + 2$
Combine like terms on the right.	$19x = 13$

STEP 4: DIVIDING BY THE COEFFICIENT

The last step is to get that x all by itself, without its coefficient. Remember how we had to change the sign on positive and negative numbers when we moved them to the other side of the equation? That's because we were changing a plus to a minus. They are inverse, or opposite, operations.

We have to do something similar with the coefficient. Since $19x$ really means 19 times x, we have to do the opposite operation when we move the 19 to the other side, which means we have to divide the other side of the equation by 19.

That means we have to make a fraction. The coefficient will become the denominator of the fraction, but you should probably show your work by multiplying each side by $^{19}/_{19}$.

So, the last step of our problem, $19x = 13$, changes to

$$\frac{\cancel{19}x}{\cancel{19}} = \frac{13}{19}$$

$$x = \frac{13}{19}$$

Simplify any fraction if you can. Sometimes, you'll end up with a whole number. In this case, we can't simplify any further, so we've solved our problem.

Believe me, once you start doing these things and getting some practice, it becomes second nature. And that's what you want, because, well, who wants to spend too much time on this stuff?

> **POSITIVELY OOPS!**
>
> One very common mistake that occurs when solving equations is to incorrectly handle positive and negative signs when transposing. When the wrong sign is attached to a number, your answer will be "negatively" affected! So look out. It's important to distribute the correct signs across expressions, and then it's important to correctly change the signs whenever transposing a number or variable from one side of an equation to the other.

YOUR TURN

Solve the following equations:

1. $(3x - 1) + 2 = (4x + 2) + 1$

2. $-7 - 3c = -5 - 2c$

3. $-5(1 + z) + 12z = 16$

4. $-3(6 - w) + 7w = 12$

5. $-9 - (-3 - 5t) = -3(7t + 4)$

6. $14x + 6 - [(3 - x) - (7x + 9)] = 15$

7. $19 - \{[3x - (x - 1)] - 5x\} = 0$

8. $4[3 - (2x + 4x) + 3x] = 6 + 2x$

9. $(4y + 7) + (3 - 2y) = 18y$

10. $3(4x - 2) + (3 - x) = 7$

5

CHAPTER 5
EQUATIONS WITH FRACTIONS

FIVE DAYS AGO

I'm sitting in the cafeteria thinking about solving equations with fractions, when I think, "I have to get a life." A life apart from algebra. Sometimes just hearing the word *algebra* gives you a little bit of a sweaty-palm feeling, right? Well, I'm here to tell you, "Nah, it's okay."

But I still have to get a life. Which is not easy to do when you can't form new memories. But I'm going to do it. And I'm going to do it by asking out the new girl, Liesa. She's French—a foreign exchange student. Being new, not only to the school, but to America, she's almost on the same footing as me. I have no memory, so I don't really have a past either. That's one reason to ask her out. Another is that she's gorgeous—just look at her sitting there in her cheerleader's uniform. I sort of have a thing for cheerleaders. . . . Yes, get a life, I know.

Do it, Ryan. Do it now. Go over there and say hi to her before you forget. Wait. She's getting up. She's taking her tray to the garbage. Do it now!

"Ryan."

No, what is it? What was I doing?

"Yo, Ryan." It's the cafeteria worker. "Are you going to take this tray you ordered, or what?" He extends a tray of coleslaw and beef Stroganoff invitingly.

"Um, I don't know. I actually feel kind of full. . . ."

"Listen, boy. Are you making fun of me?"

"No," I say. "Of course not. I have this problem where I can't form—"

"Yeah, I know. New memories. You told me. Look, just take your lunch and get outta here."

I take my tray and look around the room: a sea of unfamiliar faces. Ahh, but I am familiar with one thing: algebra—and don't laugh. Look, just because you don't like math doesn't mean you get to skip it for the rest of your life, you know. But it's okay. I'm here to help.

FRACTIONS

To solve equations with fractions, you follow the same rules you learned in Chapter 4:

1. Simplify.
2. Transpose.
3. Simplify.
4. Divide by the coefficient.

Here's an example of a variable in the numerator of the fraction (that's the top number). Follow along to see how it's done.

$$4(x + 3) - 2x = \frac{x + 1}{2} + 10$$

Remove parentheses. $$4x + 12 - 2x = \frac{x + 1}{2} + 10$$

Next, you want to get rid of the fraction. In order to do that, you have to multiply the entire equation (yes, both sides) by 2 so that the 2 in the denominator can be canceled out and your fraction will be gone. Here's how it works:

Multiply both sides by 2. $$2\left(4x + 12 - 2x = \frac{x + 1}{2} + 10\right)$$

This cancels the denominator. $$8x + 24 - 4x = \frac{\cancel{2}(x + 1)}{\cancel{2}} + 20$$

And gets rid of your fraction. $$8x + 24 - 4x = x + 1 + 20$$

Group the like terms. $$4x + 24 = x + 21$$

Transpose. $$3x = -3$$

Divide by the coefficient. $$\frac{\cancel{3}x}{\cancel{3}} = -\frac{3}{3}$$

Change to a proper fraction. $$x = -1$$

VARIABLE IN THE DENOMINATOR

Now you are ready to solve an equation with fractions that have the variable in the denominator (that's the bottom number). This type of equation is called a **fractional equation.**

Don't worry: you follow the same four golden steps. It's just that this time, you take your answer for *x* and check it by placing it in the original equation. Here's our practice problem:

$$\frac{3+x}{x} = 5$$

Simplify (clear fractions).

$$x\left(\frac{3+x}{x} = 5\right)$$

$$x\frac{3+x}{x} = 5x$$

$$\not{x}\frac{3+x}{\not{x}} = 5x$$

$$3+x = 5x$$

Transpose. $3 = 5x - x$

Simplify. $3 = 4x$

Divide by coefficient.

$$\frac{3}{4} = \frac{\not{4}x}{\not{4}}$$

$$\frac{3}{4} = x$$

We've got an answer. Now, let's put it back into the equation in place of *x* and see if it works. It will probably be easier to work with the fraction as a decimal, so let's put .75 in place of *x*.

$$\frac{3.75}{.75} = 5$$ Simplify the improper fraction.

$$5 = 5$$ Our answer checks out. Good.

FRACTIONS

TRY AGAIN

Let's try another problem that has two fractions, both with a variable in the denominator:

$$\frac{3}{x} + 3 = \frac{-1-x}{2x}$$

Simplify by multiplying the entire expression by the common denominator of the two fractions, 2x:

$$2x\left(\frac{3}{x} + 3 = \frac{-1-x}{2x}\right)$$

$$2\cancel{x}\left(\frac{3}{\cancel{x}} + 3\right) = \cancel{2x}\left(\frac{-1-x}{\cancel{2x}}\right)$$

All fractions are clear.

$$6 + 6x = -1 - x$$

Simplify.

$$6x + x = -1 - 6$$

$$7x = -7$$

$$x = \frac{-7}{7}$$

$$x = -1$$

Now, put the answer -1 back into the original problem in place of x to check your work.

$$\frac{3}{-1} + 3 = \frac{-1-(-1)}{2(-1)}$$

$$-3 + 3 = \frac{-1+1}{-2}$$

$$0 = \frac{0}{2}$$

$$0 = 0$$

Any 0 in a fraction makes the fraction equal to 0, so our answer checks out.

FRACTIONS

CROSS MULTIPLY

Now's about the time when you're wishing for a shortcut, right? Well, there is something that can help. If you're doing a fractional equation with two fractions, one on each side of the equal sign, there is a shortcut you can use. It's called cross multiplying. Here's the kind of problem you need in order to do it:

$$\frac{5}{x-1} = \frac{2}{x}$$

Just multiply across the fractions, in the shape of an *x*: the numerator of the first fraction times the denominator of the second fraction. On the other side of your equal sign, you multiply the denominator of the first fraction by the numerator of the second. Like this:

$$\frac{5}{x-1} \times \frac{2}{x}$$

$$5x = 2(x-1)$$
$$5x = 2x - 2$$
$$5x - 2x = -2$$
$$3x = -2$$

$$x = -\frac{2}{3}$$

COMMON MISTAKES

I've seen it happen countless times. You have a fractional equation staring you right in the face. You decide to get rid of that fraction by multiplying the whole equation by that pesky number in the denominator. That should clear out your fraction so you can go about solving it with ease, right? But do you know how many people only multiply across one side of the equation? That sets the whole problem off, and you've forever got an unbalanced equation after that. So, don't forget to multiply the *whole* equation by that number to clear the fraction.

YOUR TURN

Solve the following equations:

1. $x - \frac{x+1}{2} = 4x - (1 + 2x) - \frac{x}{2}$

2. $10 - \frac{3x}{5} = x - 12$

3. $2(x-2) = 5 + \frac{x-1}{4}$

4. $\frac{5}{x} = \frac{1}{2} + \frac{2+x}{x}$

5. **Check your answer to problem 4. Replace *x* with your answer.**

6. $13 + \frac{3}{x} = 12 - \frac{4}{x}$

7. **Check your answer to problem 6. Replace *x* with your answer.**

Cross multiply:

8. $\frac{8+3}{x} = \frac{5-2}{2}$

9. $\frac{15}{8x} = \frac{2}{9+x}$

10. $\frac{26}{8-r} = \frac{2}{4+r}$

6

CHAPTER 6
TWO-VARIABLE EQUATIONS

SIX DAYS AGO

Look, forget about algebra just for a moment. I promise you, I can help. Yes, I'm Ryan, and yes, I'm a tutor, and yes, you've come to the right place. You need to get a good grade, I know.

But here's what's on my mind right now. Eiffel Tower. Baguette. Black coffee. Poodles. Give up? I'm going to ask out the French girl. She's here in the cafeteria with us—the one in the cheerleader's uniform, over at that table. This is a big deal for me. Since my accident, I haven't had much of a social life, you know what I mean? It's not easy when you *can't form new memories*!

Enough is enough. I'm going over there right now to strike up a conversation with her.

"Ryan."

What? What's this?

"Ryan, you forgot to get your lunch." It's the cafeteria worker.

"Oh, sorry. I have this condition where I can't form new memories."

"Indeed. Well, here's your tray of beef Stroganoff and coleslaw."

"Thank you." I take it back to my table. But there's no place to put my tray, because there's already an identical tray of beef Stroganoff and coleslaw sitting in my place, untouched. I throw a questioning glance at the cafeteria worker.

He shrugs sheepishly.

"I thought you said I didn't get my lunch?"

"Well, look, man, they're both yours."

"Why would you give me two lunches?"

"When the manager found out about your condition, he said to keep trying to sell you extra beef Stroganoff and coleslaw."

"Huh?"

"We made too much, it's going bad, whatever."

"I appreciate your honesty."

"You're not going to remember, anyway."

"You don't have to be that honest."

But I'll be honest . . . algebra is a lot easier to deal with than beef Stroganoff. By the way, if there's some section of this book that you need to go to for help, you don't have to wait for me. You can go right to it. Whatever works for you is fine.

X AND Y IN THE SAME BOAT

Now we're getting into problems that "look" really tough—algebra equations with two different variables, such as an x and y.

$$4x + 2y = 3x - 2y$$

Isolate all the x and y variables on each side of the equation. Follow the same rules you have been using all along: simplify, transpose, simplify, and divide by the coefficient. Once you have the variables separated, you can solve for one of them. If you solve for x, the y will be in your answer. If you solve for y, the x will be in your answer. Check it out:

$$4x - 3x = -2y - 2y$$

$$x = -4y$$

And if you solve for y, the x will be in your answer:

$$4x - 3x = -2y - 2y$$

$$x = -4y$$

$$\frac{1}{4}x = y$$

FINDING X AND Y

Okay, suppose you want to find the answer for both x and y. Let's look at the example:

$$x + y = 6$$

Well, if you think about it, there are several possibilities here. Perhaps $x = 2$ and $y = 4$. But what about $x = 5$ and $y = 1$? And $x = 3{,}000$ and $y = -2{,}994$. And don't forget $x = 5.25$ and $y = .75$.

Now, that's just insane. There are an infinite number of solutions for that problem. The same would be true for any equation with two variables. We're not interested in finding a ton of different solutions to the same problem. We'd really like to find just one answer that works. This is called a **linear equation in two variables**, and it looks something like this:

$$ax + by = c$$

With this type of problem, both a and b cannot equal 0. But ya know what? One of them can equal 0.

SELECTING A VALUE FOR X

Let's look at this equation:

$$2x - y = 6$$

How can we find some solutions to this equation? Let's just select a value for one of the variables. How about x? You have to start somewhere, right? When we choose a value for x, we can plug it into the equation and find the value for y.

Let's plug in a 3 in place of *x* and see what happens:

$$2x - y + 6$$
$$2(3) - y + 6$$
$$6 - y = 6$$
$$y = 0$$

This equation works if $x = 3$ and $y = 0$. Now, try it again with x as a 5:

$$2x - y = 6$$
$$2(5) - y = 6$$
$$10 - y = 6$$
$$y = 4$$

So, another solution to the problem is $x = 5$ and $y = 4$. It's easy to go back and check it:

$$2x - y = 6$$
$$2(5) - (4) = 6$$
$$10 - 4 = 6$$
$$6 = 6$$

ORDERED PAIRS

There's a little shortcut for showing your answers to linear equations with two unknown variables: it's called an **ordered pair**. In an ordered pair, the values of the variables are usually written within a pair of parentheses, in alphabetical order of the variables. So, if $a = 7$ and $b = 6$, the ordered pair is (7, 6). If $z = 12$ and $t = 21$, the ordered pair is (21, 12).

Using the example $2x - y = 6$ from the previous section, for our first solution, we can write the ordered pair (3, 0). For the second solution, we can write the ordered pair (5, 4).

Remember that the order of the pair is important. The solution would not work if you reversed the order and substituted 0 for x and 3 for y.

IF X, THEN . . .

When you solve equations with two variables, you're solving a **conditional equation**. That's an equation that's only true for certain values. The answer for y depends on the answer for x. The two variables are related to each other within the problem.

When you take the SAT or other exams, you'll find lots of these conditional problems. You'll see them when you answer logic questions. They're expressed as "if this happens, then that happens." It's the same principle as "if x equals this, then y equals that." Get used to this type of problem. You're going to see it a lot!

YOUR TURN

1. Solve for x so that y is in your answer:
$13x + 4y = 5x - 3y$

2. Solve for n if $r = 0$:
$6r + 4n = 12$

Find the missing number so that each of the ordered pairs below is a solution to this equation: $3x + 2y = 9$

3. $(3, ?)$

4. $(-3, ?)$

5. $(?, 0)$

6. $(?, 12)$

For each equation below, determine if the given ordered pair is a solution to the equation:

7. $(3, 2)$ $2x + 3y = 12$

8. $(10, 3)$ $y = 3x + 1$

9. $(16, 4)$ $2a - 3b = 20$

10. $(3, 5)$ $8g - 3h = 8$

7

CHAPTER 7
EXPONENTS

SEVEN DAYS AGO

Listen, it's great that you could meet me here in the cafeteria. I don't always do so well at keeping appointments. I have this condition: I can't form new memories. But I can remember all my algebra classes. Sometimes people freak out when they see the word *algebra*. Or when they see the letter *x*. I'm here to say, "Nah, it's not a problem."

No problem at all. Hey, do you mind waiting for a moment while I go talk to the new girl? The French student? Why? Uh, somebody told me she was looking for an algebra tutor. Got to keep up the business. Just because you guys don't like math doesn't mean you get to skip it for the rest of your life. Here I go.

Hold on. Why are there seventeen identical trays of beef Stroganoff and coleslaw at this table? No: ignore.

"Ryan."

"Shut up. . . . Um, excuse me. Liesa?"

The pretty girl in the cheerleader's uniform looks up at me and smiles. Her eyebrows raise, questioning.

"It is Liesa, right? I'm not that good with names. *Believe me*."

Still that puzzled look. But she's smiling. That's good. Um, now she's laughing. I look around. The kids at the other tables are all staring at me.

"*Ca va*, Ryan?"

"Qu'est-ce qui se passe?"

"Bonjour, Ryan, ça va? Qu'est-ce qui se passe?"

"Arrete! Parle avec moi!"

"Tu dois lire ce livre."

"T'as oublié la stroganoff!"

"Aimes-tu le déjeuner?"

"Yo, Ryan, are you going to pick up this coleslaw, or what, man?"

You know how quickly things can get confusing when there are numbers involved? Don't freak out. It's not a problem. Nah, it's really not a problem at all.

EXPONENT BASICS

It will help to go over exponents so you're not just thrown right into algebra problems with exponents and square roots.

Here's an exponent:

$$5^2$$

The 5 is called the **base**, and the 2 is called the **exponent**. When you see a number with an exponent, it means you have to multiply the base by itself the number of times shown in the exponent. 5^2 looks like this:

$$5 \times 5 = 25$$

Same goes for 3^4. It doesn't represent 3×4. In fact, it is a short way of writing:

$$3 \times 3 \times 3 \times 3 = 81$$

Any number to the 0 power equals 1. So, $8^0 = 1$. Any number to the first power equals that number. So, $8^1 = 8$.

OPERATIONS WITH EXPONENTS

In order to add or subtract numbers with exponents, solve for each exponent first and then continue with your problem:

$$5^2 + 5^4 = (5 \times 5) + (5 \times 5 \times 5 \times 5) = 25 + 625 = 650$$

When you multiply exponents, check to see if the bases are the same. If they are, just add up the exponents and keep the base the same.

$$3^2 \times 3^4 = 3^6$$
$$3 \times 3 \times 3 \times 3 \times 3 \times 3 = 729$$

When the bases are different, solve for each exponent individually and then go on with your problem:

$$3^2 \times 4^4 = (3 \times 3) \times (4 \times 4 \times 4 \times 4) = 9 \times 256 = 2{,}304$$

The same thing goes for division problems with exponents. If the bases are the same, you can subtract the exponents and keep the base the same. If the bases are different, simplify the exponents first, and then do your division problem.

$$5^3 \div 3^2 = (5 \times 5 \times 5) \div (3 \times 3) = 125 \div 9 = 13.89$$

ORDER OF OPERATIONS

What happens when your equation or expression has more than just exponents in it? What do you do first? Just think back to the order of operations: Please Excuse My Dear Aunt Sally. That means you should do your equation in this order: Parentheses, Exponents, Multiplication, Addition, and Subtraction.

So, after you do any operations inside the parentheses (including solving exponents), you should go through and solve for any other exponents in the problem. Here's a sample:

$$2(3x + 2^2) = 4x - 3^2$$
$$2(3x + 4) = 4x - 9$$
$$6x + 8 = 4x - 9$$
$$6x - 4x = -9 - 8$$
$$2x = -17$$

$$x = -\frac{17}{2}$$

$$x = -8.5$$

It's best to check your work to see that you did it right. Put -8.5 in place of the *x* throughout the problem:

$$\begin{aligned} 2(3x + 2^2) &= 4x - 3^2 \\ 2(3 \cdot -8.5 + 2^2) &= 4 \cdot -8.5 - 3^2 \\ 2(-25.5 + 4) &= -34 - 9 \\ -51 + 8 &= -43 \\ -43 &= -43 \end{aligned}$$

ROOTS

Remember what a root, or a square root, is? It's kind of the opposite of an exponent. A **root** is a divisor of a quantity that gives you that quantity when it's squared. Since $4^2 = 16$, the square root of 16 is 4. Roots are written like this:

$$\sqrt{16} = 4$$

The square root of 16 is a perfect square. The sign around the 16 is called the **radical sign**.

Very often, you'll see a number, or coefficient, in front of a square root sign. This coefficient needs to stick to the radical and should be multiplied by any square root once it's solved:

$$3\sqrt{4} = 3(2) = 6$$

Since we can tell that the square root of 4 is 2 (because $2^2 = 4$), we multiply the coefficient of 3 times the perfect square of 2, and we get the answer 6.

SIMPLIFYING ROOTS

You might wonder what happens when your root does not work out to be a perfect square. Well, we can't get rid of it, but we can simplify it. Ask yourself what numbers can be factored out to get to perfect squares. So, when you are looking at the square root of 40, you're also looking at the square root of 4 times the square root of 10. Watch:

$$\sqrt{40} = \sqrt{4} \cdot \sqrt{10}$$

Remember, it's not the same as saying that the square root of 40 equals 4 times 10. You have to keep the radical sign over the numbers until you can find a perfect square.

Since $\sqrt{4}$ is 2, you can "pull out the square root" from the equation and have the $\sqrt{4}$ be represented by a 2. That way, you can represent it as a coefficient, like this:

$$\sqrt{40} = 2\sqrt{10}$$

Notice that there were other possibilities to choose from to simplify $\sqrt{40}$. You could have chosen $\sqrt{5} \cdot \sqrt{8}$. But that doesn't leave you with any perfect squares. The idea behind simplifying roots is get as many numbers as possible out from under the radical signs. So, think before you choose which numbers you use to simplify a root.

GROWING, GROWING, GROWN

When you increase a number by an exponent and then increase that number by an exponent as well, that number will grow out of control faster than a deadly runaway virus. Say you donate 2 cents one day to a local charity. Then you increase the amount exponentially each day—that is your donation is squared, or raised to the second power. In just a few months, you'll be donating more than a trillion dollars a day. Don't get yourself into that kind of debt! In fact, if you ever see a bank offer interest in such a manner, grab it!

YOUR TURN

1. **Rewrite this expression with exponents, then solve it:**
   $(3 \times 3 \times 3 \times 3) + (2 \times 2 \times 2)$

Solve these problems. Use the order of operations when necessary:

2. $5^5 + 8^4$

3. $4(2x + 2^2) + 4x = 6x - 3^2$

4. $(8 + 3^3) + (4 - 5^4) = x + 20$

5. $x(3^2 + 2^3) \cdot 3x(5^2) = 50$

Simplify these expressions:

6. $\sqrt{81} + \sqrt{169}$

7. $\sqrt{147}$

8. $5\sqrt{12} - 13\sqrt{27} + 17\sqrt{45}$

9. $\sqrt{5}(2 - \sqrt{3})$

10. $-2\sqrt{12} \times (-5\sqrt{3})$

CHAPTER 8
THE LAWS OF EXPONENTS

EIGHT DAYS AGO

I'm glad you've come to me for help. Your report card will thank you. I know, you probably freak out a bit when you see the word *algebra* or when you see the letter *x*. I'm here to tell you. . . .

What? You think I should ask her out? The new girl? But she just started today. Besides, she's French. Not to mention a cheerleader. That's a little out of my league, don't you think?

Okay, fine. You don't have to tell me to get a life. It's a little unkind. I have a disability, after all. Oh, you think it's time I stopped hiding behind my disability? Time that I joined the human race?

Maybe you're right. Let me just pick up this tray of coleslaw—no? You'll get it for me? How thoughtful.

"Liesa? Your name is Liesa, right? I'm a little bad with names. I have this condition—"

"Yes, you freak, my name is Liesa. Sit down. Put that tray anywhere, okay? No, I'm not French, by the way. Let's just drop that little game for two minutes, okay, sweetie?"

"Um . . ."

"You want to ask me something, Ryan? You want to ask if I'll go out with you? You want to date me—is that it?"

"Well . . ."

"Spit it out. How are you going to get a life if you don't say what you want?"

"Well, I—"

"Look, let me ask you a question. If I agreed to go out with you, how would you remember to meet me?"

"Well—"

"No, here's a better question. How do you know we haven't dated *already*?"

"Uh, I—"

“How do you know I’m not already *your girlfriend*? Look, I’m going to go take this tray over to the garbage. I want you to sit here and think about this for a minute and let me know when you’ve got your answer straightened out.”

Well, that went well, I think. Look, just because you don’t like math doesn’t mean you can skip it for the rest of your life. Yes, get a life, I know.

EXPONENT LAWS

You are about to enter into the next exciting phase of algebra. You’ve mastered expressions and equations. You will soon be a master of exponents—and with that knowledge, you can plow through just about any algebra problem that’s thrown your way. There are five laws that you need to learn and practice before you become proficient with the “power.”

MULTIPLICATION LAW

$$b^n \cdot b^m = b^{n+m}$$

I know you just learned this law in the last chapter, but let’s go over it again because there are some funky combinations that we didn’t talk about that might be worth thinking about now. The setup of numbers will not always look as straightforward as it does in the above example.

Say, for instance, you have a number to the first power. There won’t be an exponent showing above the number:

$$3 \cdot 3^4$$

So, you have to recognize that multiplying these numbers together means multiplying two exponents. Treat the 3 as 3^1. Then follow the multiplication law:

$$3 \cdot 3^4 = 3^1 \cdot 3^4 = 3^{1+4} = 3^5$$

Another example is parentheses and exponents. Remember that parentheses mean multiplication. So,

$$b^3(4b^2) = b^3 \cdot 4 \cdot b^2 = 4b^5$$

Oh, and here's a good one that you might not even recognize as something that would fit under the multiplication law:

$$(x^4y^2)(xy^3)(6xy)$$

Remember, the multiplication law applies for expressions with more than just two products. Separate each variable individually so that you can regroup them and add them up.

$$x^4 \cdot y^2 \cdot x^1 \cdot y^3 \cdot 6 \cdot x^1 \cdot y^1$$
$$6x^{4+1+1} \cdot y^{2+3+1}$$
$$6x^6y^6$$

POWER OF A POWER LAW

$$(b^n)^m = b^{nm}$$

This one is pretty easy, and it's a nice shortcut too. When you see a power raised to another power, you multiply the exponents together.

$$(7^2)^3 = 7^{2 \times 3} = 7^6$$

The parentheses should be an easy reminder to multiply.

If we try to solve this expression the long way, we have to use the multiplication law to get the same solution:

$$(7^2)^3 = (7^2)(7^2)(7^2)$$
$$7^{2+2+2} = 7^6$$

POWER OF A PRODUCT LAW

$$(bc)^n = b^n c^n$$

This law is almost exactly like the power of a power law, but it's really a reminder that if you have another variable or number inside your parentheses, it has to be changed to the same power that the variable is being changed to:

$$(4r^2)^2 = 4^2 r^4 = 16r^4$$

Even though the 4 is not expressed to any power other than 1, it has to be squared along with the r.

Sometimes, you'll find that both the terms inside the parentheses are expressed to a power:

$$(3^2 x^3 y^4)^2 = 3^4 x^6 y^8$$

In this case, each product in the expression is raised to the power that's shown on the outside of the parentheses.

POWER OF A FRACTION LAW

$$\left(\frac{a}{b}\right)^n = \frac{a^n}{b^n}$$

If you have a fraction such as $3/4$ and it has to be raised to some power, you must raise both the numerator and the denominator of the fraction to that power, like this:

$$\left(\frac{3}{4}\right)^2 = \frac{3^2}{4^2} = \frac{9}{16}$$

Of course, once you get your answer, you should simplify the fraction if possible. But this one looks like it's already simplified as far as it can go.

This same rule applies to fractions even when the numerator and denominator are already raised to a power. You're really just trying to remove parentheses when you perform the power of a fraction law, and removing parentheses means multiplication. Check out this example. We use x and y in the fraction instead of real numbers, because the numbers would get huge if we really did the math.

$$\left(\frac{x^3}{y^2}\right)^3 = \frac{x^{3 \cdot 3}}{y^{2 \cdot 3}} = \frac{x^9}{y^6}$$

DIVISION LAW

$$\frac{b^m}{b^n} = b^{m-n}$$

Need another example?

$$\frac{6^2}{6^3} = 6^{2-3} = 6^{-1} = \frac{1}{6}$$

And just for good measure, here's a third.

$$\frac{2^4}{2^2} = 2^{4-2} = 2^2 = 4$$

MIXING IT UP

Now, why learn five different laws if you're not going to combine everything and mix it all up? That's the fun and the challenge of learning something new. You can put it to use in a problem like this:

$2^3(2 \cdot 4^2)^2$

$2^3(2^2 \cdot 4^4)$ — Use the power of a product law.

$2^3 \cdot 2^2 \cdot 4^4$

$2^{3+2} \cdot 4^4$ — Use the multiplication law.

THE LAWS OF EXPONENTS

$2^5 \cdot 4^4$

$32 \cdot 256$

$8{,}192$

Here's another one to follow through:

$(4^2)^2 \times \left(\frac{6^2}{6^3}\right)^2$

$4^{2 \cdot 2} \times \left(\frac{6^2}{6^3}\right)^2$ Use the power of a power law.

$4^{2 \cdot 2} \times \frac{6^{2 \cdot 2}}{6^{3 \cdot 2}}$ Use the power of a fraction law.

$4^4 \times \frac{6^4}{6^6}$ Simplify.

$4^4 \times \frac{\cancel{6^4}}{6^{\cancel{6}}{}_2}$ Cancel out.

$256 \times \frac{1}{36}$

$\frac{64}{9} = 7.11$

PERFECT CUBES

When you think of a cube, you probably think of something with four sides, like a square or a box. Well, go figure, but when something is **cubed** in math, it's brought to the third power, not the fourth. It's very common to **cube** a number, so here's a handy list of numbers that are raised to the third power:

$1^3 = 1$	$6^3 = 216$
$2^3 = 8$	$7^3 = 343$
$3^3 = 27$	$8^3 = 512$
$4^3 = 64$	$9^3 = 729$
$5^3 = 125$	$10^3 = 1{,}000$

YOUR TURN

Which law of exponents must be used to solve these problems?

1. $4 \cdot 4^5 = 4^6$

2. $(2^3)^2$

3. $(5 \cdot 7)^3 = 5^3 \cdot 7^3$

Simplify each expression:

4. $5x^0$

5. $x^2(x^4)^5$

6. $(4x^2)^3(2x^2)^2$

7. $(x^3y)(xy^2)$

8. $\left(\frac{2^2}{3^3}\right)^2$

9. $\frac{5^4}{5^2}$

10. $\frac{(2xy)^2}{(3x^2)^3}$

9

CHAPTER 9
MULTIPLYING POLYNOMIALS

NINE DAYS AGO

Sorry, no time for algebra today. Tonight is *prom night*!

I bet you never thought a freak like me would get a date. I bet you thought a guy who *can't even form new memories* would probably have a bit of trouble lining up a date for the prom, right? You probably thought maybe one of my students, a sophomore with thick glasses who'd skipped two grades in elementary school and studies algebra to get ahead, would feel sorry for me and agree to go with me, right?

No, no. I'm going with a cheerleader. A *French* cheerleader. The very beautiful *new girl*. The girl everyone's been wanting to ask out. Yes, I know, they all had prom dates already when she arrived. Luck was on my side.

So I pick her up. Her mother and father are on the front lawn to take pictures of us in our formal attire as I pin on her corsage. I mean, the mother and father of her host family, of course. My heart is in my throat as I drive her to school. My palms are only the slightest bit sweaty as I walk through the parking lot toward the school gym. And am I fooling myself that her palms are just the slightest bit sweaty too? (It's hard to tell because my palms are sweaty.)

The door swings open; I see lights and hear the noise of a crowd inside. I slip her hand under my forearm and lead my queen triumphantly into. . . .

Wait. It's way too brightly lit to be the prom. The floor is filled with cheerleaders, not dancers. The bleachers are full of students, and they aren't in formal wear. Liesa is gone–gone to join the cheerleaders in the halftime show–of which I, it seems, am the star attraction. The entire school erupts in laughter.

You know, I'm glad I'm not going to remember this. I slip into a seat in the bleachers and hug my Gingiss tux jacket around myself. Sometimes people freak out. Like when they see the letter *x*. But I'm here to tell you. Not a problem. No problem at all.

GEARING UP

Okay, you know how to deal with many situations in algebra, including exponents, fractions, groupings in parentheses, all sorts of stuff. So, rather than have you write out expressions, distribute numbers, and show every step every time, I'll show you a good shortcut for multiplying two binomials together. But, of course, before you learn the short version, you have to learn the long version.

MULTIPLYING BINOMIALS

To multiply binomials you have to use the distributive property, but instead of distributing just one number or variable, you have to distribute a whole expression. Let's see how that works:

$(x+2)(x+7)$	
$(x+2)(x)+(x+2)(7)$	Distribute $(x+2)$.
$x^2+2x+7x+14$	Multiply.
$x^2+9x+14$	Combine terms.

Try it one more time to make sure you've got it.

$(3x-2)(x+5)$	
$(3x-2)(x)+(3x-2)(5)$	Distribute $(3x-2)$.
$3x^2-2x+15x-10$	Multiply.
$3x^2+13x-10$	Combine terms.

Got it? Good. Now learn a faster way to do it. It involves doing a little work in your head, but things will be faster and smoother once you get it.

FOIL METHOD

Here's the shortcut for multiplying two binomials:

1. Find the product of the two **first** terms of the binomials.
2. Find the product of the two **outermost** terms.
3. Find the product of the two **innermost** terms.
4. Find the product of the two **last** terms.

We can use a good memorization aid to remember those steps. **F**irst, **O**uter, **I**nner, **L**ast, or **FOIL**.

So let's look at the first example again:

$$(x+2)(x+7)$$

This is what the terms look like:

first: $(x+2)(x+7)$	The first terms are $x \cdot x$ or x^2.
outer: $(x+2)(x+7)$	The outer terms are $7x$.
inner: $(x+2)(x+7)$	The inner terms are $2x$.
last: $(x+2)(x+7)$	The last terms are 2×7 or 14.

So, we can rewrite $(x+2)(x+7)$ as

$$(x+2)(x+7)$$
$$x^2+7x+2x+14$$
$$x^2+9x+14$$

As you keep doing this and get more practice, you will see that you end up with a $2x$ and $7x$ and can skip a step and add them right away.

SQUARING A BINOMIAL

Here's another rule to remember:

$$(a+b)^2 = a^2+2ab+b^2$$
$$(a-b)^2 = a^2-2ab+b^2$$

Let's try it with $(7y+6)^2$:

$(7y+6)^2$	Square the first and last terms.
$(7y)^2+2(42y)+6^2$	Double the product of the middle terms.
$49y^2+84y+36$	Simplify.

MULTIPLYING POLYNOMIALS

When you multiply two polynomials, you might need to go back to the distribution method. When you have a trinomial and a binomial, you have to distribute each term in the binomial so that it gets factored with each term in the polynomial.

$(5x+4)(2x^2-3x+7)$	
$10x^3-15x^2+35x+8x^2-12x+28$	Distribute.
$10x^3-7x^2+23x+28$	Combine terms.

Do this for as many terms as necessary. This particular problem distributes out to six terms, but then you can combine the like terms at the end.

MEMORY TRICKS

A **mnemonic** is a system meant to improve our memory. It can be a formula, a rhyme, or an acronym like FOIL. It's a lot easier to memorize the word *foil* than to remember "first, outer, inner, last." You're much more likely to forget the words or to remember them in the wrong order if you don't use a mnemonic aid. Something like *foil* not only tells you the order in which you should do steps in an algebraic problem; it's also easier to remember because you can picture something in your head.

YOUR TURN

Simplify the following expressions:

1. $(6x + 2)(x + 9)$

2. $(4x + 3)(x - 1)$

3. $(5b + 3)(3b - 2)$

4. $(6z - 4)(6z + 4)$

5. $(12xy - 2)(3xy + 7)$

6. $(5y + 7)^2$

7. $(8z - 5)^2$

8. $(x + 1)(x^2 - 3x + 2)$

9. $(3x^2 + 5x + 1)(2x - 1)$

10. $(y - 1)(3y^2 + 4y + 2)$

10

CHAPTER 10
WORD PROBLEMS

TEN DAYS AGO

What do people really mean by "get a life"? What, exactly, does a life consist of? Some would say friends. Some would say *girl*friends. But what about family? What about a mother's love?

What about a sense of purpose? Having something that you're good at—like algebra. Being able to help others, like with tutoring.

Here I am, in the school hallway. Life moves all around me, a river of bodies. Sometimes I think all I have to do to get a life is reach out and touch it. How beautiful life is! Just look at that girl in the cheerleader's uniform.

"Put your hand down, Ryan. Do you think I'd let you touch me? You're a freak. A *freak,* do you hear me? How could you? How could you *do it*? You're disgusting. You. Disgust. Me. And you did it for what? For *her*. Your taste in women is pretty sick, Ryan. That's all I'm going to say. No, it's not. I have something else to say. You *humiliated* me, Ryan. And now I'm going to humiliate you. I'll tell you exactly what I'm going to do to you, and you're not even going to remember—you freak! For starters, I'm putting on a one-man freak show at the big game tomorrow night, and you're the star attraction. You're going to Gingiss to rent a tux tonight. Don't worry—I put the order form and 'prom' invitation in your locker so you won't forget. I know how you like to get things in writing. (Freak.) Then I'm going to tell all my friends in the French club just what a *freak* you are. We'll have a little something in store for you."

I know what Shakespeare has to say about getting a life: "And yet to me, what is this quintessence of dust? Man delights not me—no, nor woman neither." And just because you don't like math doesn't mean you get to skip it for the rest of your life, okay?

PROBLEMS WITH A VARIABLE

Let's think for a minute about why word problems even exist in this world. They're meant to solve a problem or an unknown variable, just like algebra does. So, solving an algebraic word problem seems like the ultimate mastery of algebra, doesn't it?

Well, here's an example of what I mean:

Six times a number is decreased by 8, and the result is 4 more than 3 times the number. What is that number?

Let's rewrite that with x plugged in as *a number*. We can also substitute words like *decrease* with a minus sign and *result* with an equal sign. You know: translate it into algebra.

$$6x - 8 = 4 + 3x$$

Now, let's solve the equation:

$6x - 8 = 4 + 3x$	
$6x - 3x = 4 + 8$	Transpose.
$3x = 12$	Combine terms.
$x = \frac{12}{3}$	Isolate the variable.
$x = 4$	Simplify.

Don't you think it's a good idea to plug the 4 into the original problem in place of the x to check our handiwork? It definitely is a good idea.

Our answer is correct: $x = 4$ because the problem works only when we plug 4 into the equation in place of x. The two sides of the equation balance, or equal each other.

$$\begin{aligned} 6x - 8 &= 4 + 3x \\ 6(4) - 8 &= 4 + 3(4) \\ 24 - 8 &= 4 + 12 \\ 16 &= 16 \end{aligned}$$

WORD PROBLEM CHEAT SHEET

Here's a list of common word-problem phrases that translate into algebra. You'll see a lot of these over and over again.

Word Problem Lingo	Math Translation
x is equal to 5 x is the same as 5 x is 5 x and 5 are equivalent	$x = 5$
x and 4 The sum of x and 4 x added to 4 x increased by 4 x more than 4	$x + 4$
Less than x x minus 7 x take away 7 x decreased by 7 x less 7 The difference of x and 7	$x - 7$
x times 9 The product of x and 9 x multiplied by 9	$9x$
x divided by 6 The quotient of x and 6 6 divided into x	$\frac{x}{6}$
$\frac{2}{3}$ of x 27% of x	$\frac{2}{3}x$ $.27x$

WORD PROBLEMS

WORD PROBLEMS WITH LINEAR EQUATIONS

Okay, let's try another word problem.

The sum of three consecutive integers is -102. What are the integers?

Should we set this up as a problem with three variables? No. The reason is that the problem asks for three consecutive numbers. That can be written as x, $x + 1$, and $x + 2$. That way, you only have to find x, and then you can find the consecutive numbers when you're finished.

$$x + (x + 1) + (x + 2) = -102$$
$$x + x + 1 + x + 2 = -102$$
$$3x + 3 = -102$$
$$3x = -102 - 3$$
$$3x = -105$$
$$x = -\frac{105}{3}$$
$$x = -35$$

So $x = -35$. But don't forget that you have to find three consecutive integers. Remember that adding negative numbers is a little like subtracting them. So, instead of the consecutive numbers being 35, 36, and 37, we have to stop and look at the signs first. Consecutive negative numbers would be -35, -34, and -33. You can plug them into the original equation to check your answers:

$$-35 + (-34) + (-33) = -102$$
$$-35 - 34 - 33 = -102$$
$$-102 = -102$$

WORD PROBLEMS WITH TWO UNKNOWNS

Sometimes, word problems need to be read a hundred times before you can figure out what they're saying. But once you crack the code and figure out what they're really asking you, it's no problem writing out your equation and solving it like a pro.

The sum of two numbers is 36. Their difference is 6. What are the two numbers?

Whenever there's a relationship between the two variables, you can use an equation to express that relationship. For example, we see in the word problem that the difference between the two variables is 6. That's a real number that can be used to subtract one from another, so one of the variables can be expressed as $x - 6$. We also know from reading the word problem that the sum of the two variables is 36. Let's write the equation out and solve it:

$$x + (x - 6) = 36$$
$$2x - 6 = 36$$
$$2x = 36 + 6$$
$$2x = 42$$
$$x = \frac{42}{2}$$
$$x = 21$$

So, one number equals 21. If the other variable equals $x - 6$, then it should equal $21 - 6$, or 15. Let's plug those numbers into the original problem:

$$21 + 15 = 36$$

PUZZLING PROBLEMS

Word problems are among the most feared of all math problems. This might be because word problems take a lot of concentration, and you are figuring out the answers to some rather odd and confusing questions. Lewis Carroll's classic book *Through the Looking Glass* expressed this type of frustration with nonsensical problems:

"Can you do addition?" the White Queen asked. "What's one and one and one and one and one and one and one and one and one and one?" "I don't know," said Alice. "I lost count."

Unlike Alice, you now know how to tackle word problems, so you won't lose count.

YOUR TURN

Write expressions that show the following problems in mathematical terms:

1. One number is $^4/_5$ of another.
2. Margo is three times older than Sara.
3. Jeff has eight times as many quarters as Mike.
4. Two numbers are consecutive integers.
5. The width of a rectangle is seven more than three times its length.
6. Five times a number decreased by nine is equal to another number.

Solve the following word problems:

7. The sum of two consecutive integers is 39. Find the integers.
8. Nine less than three times a number is equal to three more than twice the number. Find the number.
9. Laura is six times older than Kate. The sum of their ages is 28. How old are Laura and Kate?
10. Find three consecutive integers such that the sum of the first two decreased by 11 is equal to the third.

11

CHAPTER 11
GRAPHING COORDINATES

ELEVEN DAYS AGO

"Ryan, listen to me. What I have to tell you is *trés* important."

I'm sitting in, of all places, Craig's living room. A room I haven't seen since the sixth grade. I'm sitting in one of those plush, antique chairs, across from Craig's mother. I'm holding a Wedgwood demitasse filled with coffee.

Craig's lovely mother. She's wearing a housedress with three-quarter-length sleeves turned up and buttoned at the cuffs, the kind women used to wear in France a hundred years ago. The dress is made of white silk damask, with a pattern of interlocking peacocks and birds-of-paradise. A white pair of Manolo Blahniks twine up her ankles like twin albino garter snakes. She shifts in her chair and puts down her coffee.

"Ryan, you have to be careful. Some people will try to take advantage of your disability. A girl like Liesa is no good for you. Stay away from her."

She pauses, regarding me thoughtfully. I can smell her perfume, quietly enveloping me in its lazily provocative way. *Arpège* by Lanvin, I think.

"I'm sorry about yesterday. You must think I'm crazy—or you would if you remembered. I wore that silly getup because I thought if I made you relive that day all those years ago, it might shock you into getting your memory back. Obviously, it didn't work."

I sip my coffee. The cup clatters nervously against the saucer.

"You're like a son to me, Ryan. You know that, don't you? I will never let anything serious happen to you. Even the principal is not your friend, but you don't need to worry about him. I have friends on the school board." She rises. "Take care of yourself, Ryan."

Then she leans over me. I smell coriander, heart of rose, mimosa, jasmine, and geranium. It makes me slightly dizzy.

She plants a kiss on my cheek.

Ryan Hall. Algebra tutor *extraordinaire*. I like the sound of that.

GRAPH BASICS

I always thought graphs were pretty fun. They're a good break from solving endless problems, and it's kind of a visual thing instead of a mathematical thing.

In algebra, graphs are broken into four sections called **quadrants**. They're always numbered the same way. The top right is numbered I (with a Roman numeral), the top left is numbered II, the bottom left is III, and the bottom right is IV. Here's how that looks:

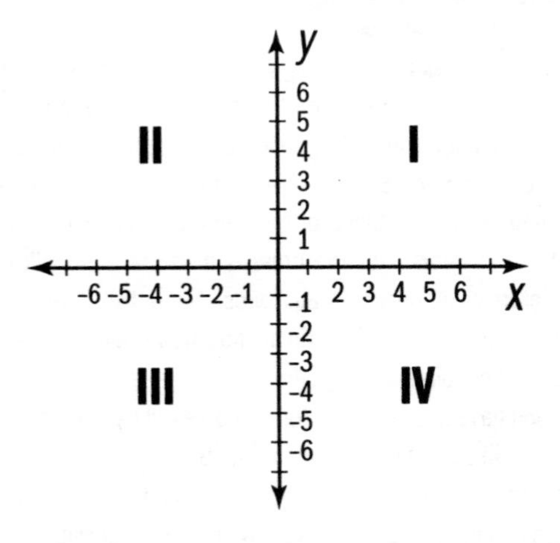

Also, the **horizontal axis**, or the line across, is usually called x. The **vertical axis**, or the line up and down, is usually called y. The point where they cross in the center is 0. That's because the x- and y-axes represent number lines. They show both positive and negative numbers, and 0 is where they both cross and meet up with each other.

Let's go over that:

1. The x-axis is a horizontal number line.
2. The y-axis is a vertical number line.
3. The center where the axes cross is 0.
4. The four quadrants are labeled I, II, III, and IV.

ORDERED PAIRS

Remember back in Chapter 6, we talked about solving equations with two variables? In order to save space and time, the answers to each variable were written as an **ordered pair**. That looks something like this: (4, 7). It's written to represent (x, y). That means in an equation with an x variable and a y variable, $x = 4$ and $y = 7$. So (4, 7) is faster and easier.

When you think of graphing, the whole ordered pair thing takes on new meaning. You can actually use the 4 and the 7 and plot them on a graph. Think about it. The 4 is a positive number. That means it belongs on the x-axis in the positive section. The 7 is positive and belongs along the vertical y-axis. If you plot these two numbers on the graph, you end up in quadrant I.

Here's how you plot the coordinates (4, 7):

1. Start at the 0 (the center, or origin).
2. Move along the x-axis 4 spaces.
3. Move up the y-axis 7 spaces.
4. Draw a dot. That's (4, 7) on the graph.

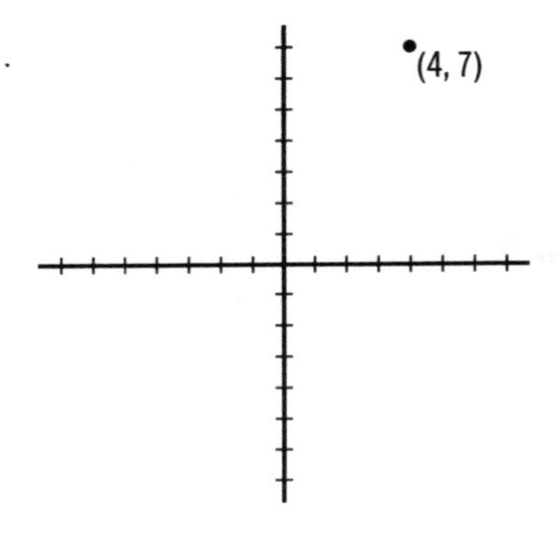

NEGATIVE COORDINATES

When you have negative numbers in your ordered pair, that means you will end up with a point plotted in either quadrant III or IV. See what I mean. Plot (–3, –6).

1. Start at the 0 center, or origin.
2. Move along the *x*-axis negative 3 spaces.
3. Move down the *y*-axis negative 6 spaces.
4. Draw a dot. You're in quadrant III.

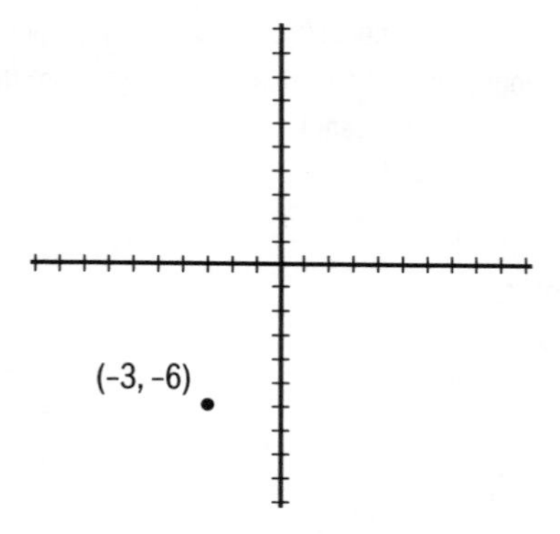

A good guideline to remember when plotting coordinates is to treat the *x*-axis and *y*-axis like number lines. On the *x*-axis, numbers to the right of 0 are positive. Numbers to the left of 0 are negative.

The same thing goes for the *y*-axis. Numbers above the 0 are positive. Numbers below the 0 are negative.

- If *x* is positive, move to the right.
- If *x* is negative, move to the left.
- If *y* is positive, move up.
- If *y* is negative, move down.

LETTERED COORDINATES

Okay, you can probably imagine that this coordinate stuff gets pretty messy if you put several dots on the same graph. Here's the math-world solution to that problem: Letter the coordinate pairs.

For example, we want to plot the following coordinates:

A (-2, 0)
B (5, 2)
C (-1, -1)
D (6, -3)

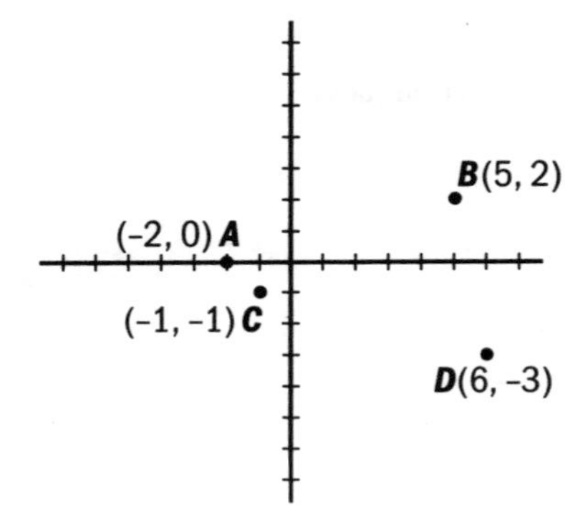

CARTESIAN SYSTEM

Have you heard of the famous French philosopher and mathematician René Descartes? He really knew his stuff. We owe our whole graphing system to his work in the early half of the 1600s. He was the first person to use two perpendicular number lines (the *x*- and the *y*-axes) to plot points. In his honor, the graph with four quadrants that we use is named after him. It's called the **Cartesian coordinate system.**

YOUR TURN

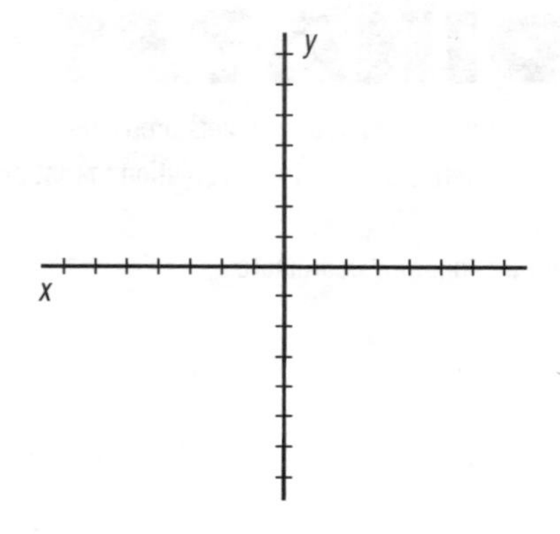

In which quadrant would the following ordered pairs be plotted?

1. (-2, 4)
2. (3, 5)
3. (2, -6)
4. (-3, -3)

Plot these ordered pairs:

5. A (3, 4)
6. B (-4, 2)
7. C (-5, -4)

What would the ordered pair be if you start at the center origin and do the following?

8. Move along the *x*-axis negative 5 spaces. Move along the *y*-axis positive 4 spaces.
9. Move along the *x*-axis 0 spaces. Move along the *y*-axis -3 spaces.
10. Move along the *x*-axis a positive half-space. Move along the *y*-axis negative 2 spaces.

12

CHAPTER 12
LINEAR EQUATIONS

TWELVE DAYS AGO

Just walking up Craig's driveway is enough to send me soaring down memory lane. I'm hit by a hundred flashbacks of the two of us skateboarding there and nearly breaking our necks daring each other to do stupid tricks. I feel fine about tutoring Craig for the first time, but I have this nervous feeling in the pit of my stomach about seeing his mom again. I ring the bell and Craig answers.

"Look, Ryan, you can go ahead in and have your cookie or whatever, but I have better things to do."

"Now, Craig, just because you don't like math doesn't mean you get to skip it for the rest of your life. I know you probably want to be out playing basketball, but your report card will thank you."

"Dude, I'm in calculus now. Algebra was *four years ago.* I haven't been on the basketball team since junior high. The only reason you come here every day is that my mom feels sorry for you. Jeez, it's like talking to a brick wall. I'm outta here."

Craig's living room looks just the same as it did—plush antique chairs upholstered in silk, comfy sofas, flowers on the side tables.

"Oh, Ryan, did that idiot boyfriend of mine leave?"

I turn around to confront a very pretty girl in a cheerleader's uniform.

"Is it true you have no memory, or is all that just a game?"

"Do we know each other?"

"Sit down, Ryan. Yes, here on this nice sofa. No, next to me. Now, if you really have no memory, we can do whatever we want, right? No one will ever find out. No consequences." She twines her arms around my neck. "Come here . . ."

"*Liesa!* Ryan. I'm surprised at you!"

There, in the doorway, bearing a silver tray with two cookies and two half-full glasses of milk, stands Craig's mom. *Wearing a cheerleader's uniform.* With its River Dell High colors and bold *X* insignia, it's identical to that worn by the girl on the sofa next to me, whom I've never seen before in my life.

My palms are sweaty. My tongue feels thick. The three of us look at each other for a long moment. Finally, I break the silence.

"Er, Mrs. G. You look . . . just as beautiful as you did when we were kids."

Liesa sobs and runs out the front door.

Some people freak out when they see the letter *x*. I'm here to tell you, Nah, it's not a problem.

LINEAR EQUATIONS

Now that you know the basics of graphing, you can solve equations, plot them on a graph, and make a straight line. Well, you can't just solve *any* old equation and plot it in a straight line. There are certain rules, as you have learned to expect in algebra. (There are always rules!)

In order to plot a line on a graph from an equation, you have to solve a linear equation. Here's what's involved in a linear equation:

1. There are two variables.
2. The variables are involved with the four basic operations (addition, subtraction, multiplication, or division).
3. Neither variable is raised to a power (other than 1).
4. Neither variable is in a denominator of a fraction.
5. No term in the equation shows the variables as a product.

Not that you have to memorize any of this stuff—it's just that it's good to know what you can graph and what you can't graph.

SOLVING FOR TWO VARIABLES

Let's review how to solve for two variables. We did it in Chapter 6, so it shouldn't be too much of a surprise for you. You can always go back to that chapter if you want to review the gory details of it all.

Now remember, we're going to choose a number to plug in for *x* so that we can find a pair to place with it as the *y* coordinate. Let's do this example:

$$4x + 2y = 10$$

Let's put in a 2 for the *x* coordinate and see what we get for *y*.

$$\begin{aligned} 4(\mathbf{2}) + 2y &= 10 \\ 8 + 2y &= 10 \\ 2y &= 10 - 8 \\ 2y &= 2 \; y = \frac{2}{2} \\ y &= 1 \end{aligned}$$

So, one ordered pair for this equation would be (2, 1). Plug both the variables into the original equation to check your work:

$$\begin{aligned} 4x + 2y &= 10 \\ 4(\mathbf{2}) + 2(\mathbf{1}) &= 10 \\ 8 + 2 &= 10 \\ 10 &= 10 \end{aligned}$$

But remember, (2, 1) is only one possible answer. You can enter any number for *x* in order to get *y*. But if you plan to graph the coordinates, you might as well pick a nice easy number that's on your graph. That way, it will be easy to plot, right? Why make things hard on yourself?

MORE POSSIBILITIES

Let's get a couple more coordinates that will fit into our equation. First, let's solve it with *x* as 1:

$$
\begin{aligned}
4x + 2y &= 10 \\
4(\mathbf{1}) + 2y &= 10 \\
4 + 2y &= 10 \\
2y &= 10 - 4 \\
2y &= 6 \\
y &= \frac{6}{2} \\
y &= 3
\end{aligned}
$$

So, another coordinate pair is (1, 3). Don't forget to check it:

$$
\begin{aligned}
4(\mathbf{1}) + 2(\mathbf{3}) &= 10 \\
4 + 6 &= 10 \\
10 &= 10
\end{aligned}
$$

Let's do one more. How about x as 4:

$$
\begin{aligned}
4x + 2y &= 10 \\
4(\mathbf{4}) + 2y &= 10 \\
16 + 2y &= 10 \\
2y &= 10 - 16 \\
2y &= -6 \\
y &= -\frac{6}{2} \\
y &= -3
\end{aligned}
$$

Our third ordered pair for this equation is (4, -3). Of course, give it a check by plugging in x and y:

$$
\begin{aligned}
4(\mathbf{4}) + 2(-\mathbf{3}) &= 10 \\
16 + (-6) &= 10 \\
16 - 6 &= 10 \\
10 &= 10
\end{aligned}
$$

PLOTTING THE COORDINATES

Okay. We have three ordered pairs solved for one linear equation. That should give us plenty to work with when we go to plot points on our graph.

Now let's take our three coordinate pairs and plot them:

- (2, 1)
- (1, 3)
- (4, -3)

Then take some sort of straight edge—a ruler, a piece of paper, anything straight that you can use to make a straight line. Now connect all three plot points on your graph and make a straight line.

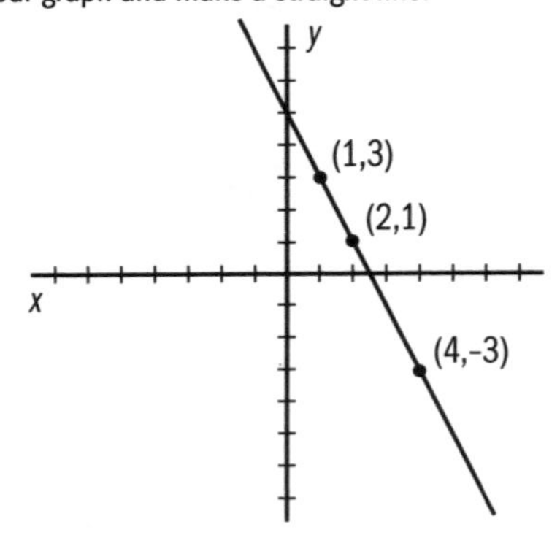

That line represents the linear equation $4x + 2y = 10$. Cool, huh?

INTERCEPT

The intercept of a line is the point where the line you make crosses the *y*-axis. It's called the *y*-intercept. Take a look at the line you made. Where exactly does it cross the *y*-axis? It crosses the *y*-axis at 5, right? So the ***y*-intercept** of your line is 5.

And yes, you guessed it. The place where your line crosses the *x*-axis is called the ***x*-intercept**. In our example, the *x*-intercept is 2.5.

DID YOU KNOW?

Here are some interesting facts about graphing. Look at your linear equation. If the coefficient of x is negative, your line will slant, or slope, to the left. If the coefficient of x is positive, the line will slope to the right. Two lines are parallel if they have the same slant, or slope.

The fastest way to convert a linear equation into a line on a graph is to assign x as 0 and solve for y. Then assign y as 0 and solve for x. You'll have two quick points to plot to make a line.

YOUR TURN

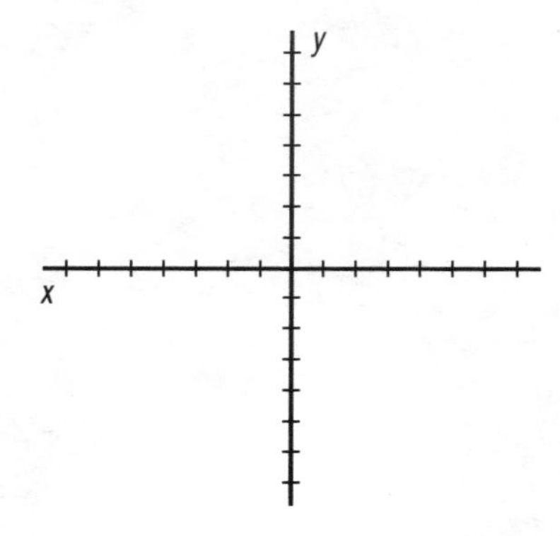

Use the following equation for questions 1, 2, and 3:

$$5x + 2y = 10$$

1. Write an ordered pair for this equation, where $x = 4$.
2. Find another ordered pair where $x = -2$.
3. Find another ordered pair where $y = 0$.

Use your ordered pairs to answer questions 4, 5, and 6.

4. Check and show your work for the ordered pair in question 1.
5. Check and show your work for the ordered pair in question 2.
6. Check and show your work for the ordered pair in question 3.

Use the above graph for questions 7 to 10.

7. Plot your three ordered pairs on the graph to make a line.
8. What is the y-intercept of your line?
9. What is the x-intercept of your line?
10. Does the ordered pair (4, 5) intercept the line that you drew? How can you tell without plotting it?

13

CHAPTER 13
TIPS

THIRTEEN DAYS AGO

Now, I know you're not too interested in math. But it's never too late to learn.

"Ryan, let's get one thing straight. You're not an algebra tutor."

"Look, just because you don't like math doesn't mean you get to just skip it for the rest of your life."

"Ryan, I'm the school principal. I think I'd know if you were an authorized tutor."

"Algebra is my life."

"Ryan, you're not even good at math. I would never assign you as a tutor because you didn't even pass algebra. You had your accident before the final."

"I have algebra equations tattooed all over my body. Did you know that?"

"One of your crazy skater friends did that to you the day of your accident. You were planning to cheat on the final, apparently. Now, I have something to say to you that you're not going to like. I can't let you keep coming to school. Your memory isn't coming back, and you haven't made any progress in four years."

"I want to help people."

The principal sighs and shifts in his seat. "As soon as the board clears this decision, you will be removed from the school. I'm sorry, Ryan."

You know, if you want to read this book from cover to cover, that's just fine. But if you'd rather, you can look up key topics you're having trouble with and just shoot right to that section.

I'm Ryan. Algebra tutor *extraordinaire*.

People sometimes freak out when they see the letter x. I'm here to say, "Nah, it's not a problem."

CHECKING YOUR ANSWERS

What's the most popular tip or word of advice from anyone when they talk to you about math? Check your work. Check your work. And check your work. You hear it so much, it's completely annoying.

Who wants to repeat a whole long problem again as soon as they finally get through it? You probably figure that if you did make any mistakes the first time around, you'll likely end up making those same mistakes the second time around. Or maybe you'll make new mistakes the second time.

Well, there is one really good thing about algebra in terms of checking your work. Once you find the value for your variable, you can go back and plug it into the original problem as a way to double-check your work. That way, you're not repeating the same steps. You're doing a new problem with new calculations, and you're checking your work at the same time.

One drawback to that, however, is that if you get the wrong answer, you can't find out what you did wrong. You still have to go back to the original problem and go over your work the old-fashioned way by repeating your steps and checking your calculations.

SHOWING YOUR WORK

You've heard this one before too. Show your work. That's probably the second most annoying tip that people give you in math. Unfortunately, they are right.

Did you know that most standardized tests have multiple-choice answers? Great, you say. You won't have to show your work. You can just choose an answer from the list. Well, think again, my friend. Teachers sometimes want to see your work anyway. And it's a good idea too. That way, the teacher knows that you didn't cheat, that you didn't guess, and that you have some idea of how to solve the problem. Sometimes, partial credit can be given for setting up your problem and showing your work even if your calculations are incorrect. So, keep your records legible. It might help you in the long run.

PRACTICE, PRACTICE, PRACTICE

This is another one of those annoying math tips you always hear: practice, practice, practice. Sorry again, but this one is true also.

Keep solving problems. Keep isolating variables. Keep reviewing what you don't know. Keep asking about what you don't understand. It's never too late to understand something. You can make a big difference on a test score or on a final grade if you keep trying. Nobody is born knowing all of these algebra rules. It's just not normal, and it's not common sense either. There are some really specific things that you have to practice and commit to memory so that you don't forget and so that you can pick up speed for tests.

A FINAL FAREWELL

Well, I've said all that I want to say about algebra. I'm going to leave you with one final Your Turn section to chew on. You'll see a question or so from just about every chapter in the book. Go back and check out how to do a particular problem if you're stumped. Looking back in the book is definitely encouraged. Good luck with your algebra work.

DON'T STRESS IT

Math is the number-one stress class for students in the United States. More students complain about not understanding math than about any other topic. And why not? It's really like speaking another language. Many number concepts are very abstract, and there are many symbols to learn. But it's all relative. Be glad you're not taking an advanced math class! As the brilliant mathematician and scientist Albert Einstein once said, "Do not worry about your difficulties in mathematics. I assure you that mine are greater."

YOUR TURN

1. Find the absolute value:
   $| -22 | + | 14 |$

2. Simplify the expression:
   $2\{x - 3[4 - (x + 1)] + 1\}$

3. Solve the equation:
   $(14n + 3n) + 2(5 + n) = 12 + 2n$

4. Solve the fractional expression:

   $$\frac{4 + 3x}{2} + 2x + \frac{5x - 1}{2}$$

5. Solve the equation for y if $x = 2$:
   $4x + 14y = 12x + 2$

Solve the equation or expression:

6. $3(2x + 2^2) = 5x - 3^2$

7. $3^2(3^3)^4$

8. $(6x - 2)(x + 7)$

9. The sum of three consecutive numbers equals 45. Find those numbers.

10. Finish the ordered pair (2, ?) using this equation:
    $3x + 4y = 14$

TIPS

ANSWER KEY

CHAPTER 1

1. y
2. expression
3. 19
4. $12x$
5. $x + y$
6. $9 + 8x$
7. $8x - x$
8. $x - 1 + y$
9. $3x + 5y$
10. $450 \cdot 11 + 2x$
11. 4 times a number plus 0
12. 81 times a number minus another number
13. 2 times a number plus 3 times another number
14. 7 plus a number
15. 12 times a number minus 3 times another number

CHAPTER 2

1. 2
2. 0
3. 7
4. $|142|$
5. 40
6. -4

   8 - 4 = 4. Make the 4 negative because the largest absolute value, 8, is negative.

7. 8

   14 - 6 = 8. Keep the 8 positive because the absolute value of 14 is positive.

8. -3

   Add the opposite of -2, which is 2. So, -5 + 2 = -3.

9. -15

Add the opposite of +7, which is -7. So, -8 + (-7) = -15.

10. 70

Add the opposite of -30, which is 30. So, 40 + 30 = 70.

11. 32

$8 \times 4 = 32$. Make the answer positive because the signs are same.

12. 42

$14 \times 3 = 42$. Make the answer positive because the signs are both negative.

13. -45

$5 \times 9 = 45$. Use the negative sign because the signs are different.

14. -165

$11 \times 15 = 165$. Use the negative sign because the signs are different.

15. -6

$12 \div 2 = 6$. Use the negative sign because the signs are different.

16. 5

$20 \div 4 = 5$. Keep the sign positive because both signs are same.

17. -17

9 + 8 = 17. Make the sign negative because both signs are negative.

18. -11

14 - 3 = 11. Make the sign negative because the 14 is negative.

19. -12

Add the opposite of 17, which is -17. 17 - 5 = 12. Keep the sign negative because the 17 is negative.

20. -40

$4 \times 10 = 40$. Make the sign negative because the signs are different.

CHAPTER 3

1. $14x + 14y$

$14(x + y)$

$14x + 14y$

2. $17x + 8$

$5(x - 4) + 4(3x + 7)$

$5x - 20 + 12x + 28$

$17x + 8$

3. $-5 + 3x$

$x - [7 - 2(x + 1)]$

$x - [7 - 2x - 2]$

$x - 7 + 2x + 2$

$x - 5 + 2x$

$-5 + 3x$

4. $39x - 20$

$5(7x - 3 + x) - (x + 5)$

$35x - 15 + 5x - x - 5$

$39x - 20$

5. $3 - 13x$

$-3(4 + x) - 5[x - (3 - x)]$

$-3(4 + x) - 5[x - 3 + x]$

$-12 - 3x - 5x + 15 - 5x$

$3 - 13x$

6. $10y + 3x$
$y(8 + 2) + x(4 - 1)$
$8y + 2y + 4x - x$
$10y + 3x$

7. $-6y^2 + 10y - 10x$
$3y(4 - 2y) - 2[y + (3x + 2x)]$
$3y(4 - 2y) - 2[y + 3x + 2x]$
$12y - 6y^2 - 2y - 6x - 4x$
$-6y^2 + 10y - 10x$

8. $8y - 20$
$2\{y - 3(6 - [2 + y]) + 3\} - 2$
$2\{y - 3(6 - 2 - y) + 3\} - 2$
$2\{y - 18 + 6 + 3y + 3\} - 2$
$2y - 36 + 12 + 6y + 6 - 2$
$8y - 20$

9. $-16 - 2x$
$4 + 2(x - 2[5 + x])$
$4 + 2(x - 10 - 2x)$
$4 + 2x - 20 - 4x$
$-16 - 2x$

10. $(65 + 4x)x$
$14(2x + 3x) - x(5 - 4x)$
$28x + 42x - 5x + 4x^2$
$65x + 4x^2$ or
$(65 + 4x)x$

CHAPTER 4

1. $x = -2$

   $(3x - 1) + 2 = (4x + 2) + 1$

   $3x - 1 + 2 = 4x + 2 + 1$ Simplify.

   $3x + 1 = 4x + 3$

   $3x = 4x + 3 - 1$ Transpose.

   $3x - 4x = 3 - 1$

   $-x = 2$ Simplify.

   $x = -2$ Divide by the coefficient.

2. $c = -2$

   $-7 - 3c = -5 - 2c$

   $-3c = -5 - 2c + 7$ Transpose.

   $-3c = -2c + 2$

   $-3c + 2c = 2$ Transpose.

   $-1c = 2$ Simplify.

   $c = -\frac{2}{1}$ Divide by the coefficient.

   $c = -2$

3. $z = 3$

   $-5(1 + z) + 12z = 16$

   $-5(1) - 5(z) + 12z = 16$ Simplify.

   $-5 - 5z + 12z = 16$

   $7z = 16 + 5$ Transpose.

   $7z = 21$ Simplify.

   $z = \frac{21}{7}$ Divide by the coefficient.

   $z = 3$

4. $w = 3$

$-3(6 - w) + 7w = 12$

$-3(6) - 3(-w) + 7w = 12$ Simplify.

$-18 + 3w + 7w = 12$

$-18 + 10w = 12$

$10w = 12 + 18$ Transpose.

$10w = 30$ Simplify.

$w = \frac{30}{10}$ Divide by the coefficient.

$w = 3$

5. $t = -\frac{3}{13}$

$-9 - (-3 - 5t) = -3(7t + 4)$

$-9 + 3 + 5t = -21t - 12$ Distribute on both sides.

$-6 + 5t = -21t - 12$ Simplify.

$5t = -21t - 12 + 6$ Transpose.

$5t = -21t - 6$ Transpose.

$21t + 5t = -6$ Simplify again.

$26t = -6$

$t = -\frac{6}{26}$ Divide by the coefficient.

$t = -\frac{3}{13}$ Simplify.

6. $x = \frac{3}{22}$

$14x + 6 - [(3 - x) - (7x + 9)] = 15$

$14x + 6 - [3 - x - 7x - 9] = 15$ Simplify.

$14x + 6 - [-6 - 8x] = 15$

$14x + 6 + 6 + 8x = 15$

$22x + 12 = 15$ Transpose.

$22x = 15 - 12$

$22x = 3$

Simplify.

$x = \frac{3}{22}$ Divide by the coefficient.

7. $x = -6$

$19 - \{[3x - (x - 1)] - 5x\} = 0$

$19 - \{[3x - x + 1] - 5x\} = 0$

$19 - \{2x + 1 - 5x\} = 0$

$19 - \{-3x + 1\} = 0$

$19 + 3x - 1 = 0$

$18 + 3x = 0$

$3x = -18$

$x = -\frac{18}{3}$

$x = -6$

8. $x = \frac{3}{7}$

$4[3 - (2x + 4x) + 3x] = 6 + 2x$

$4[3 - 2x - 4x + 3x] = 6 + 2x$

$4[3 - 3x] = 6 + 2x$

$12 - 12x = 6 + 2x$

$-12x - 2x = 6 - 12$

$-14x = -6$

$14x = 6$

$x = \frac{6}{14}$

$$x = \frac{3}{7}$$

9. $y = \frac{5}{8}$

$(4y + 7) + (3 - 2y) = 18y$

$4y + 7 + 3 - 2y = 18y$

$2y + 10 = 18y$

$10 = 18y - 2y$

$10 = 16y$

$$\frac{10}{16} = y$$

$$\frac{5}{8} = y$$

10. $x = \frac{10}{11}$

$3(4x - 2) + (3 - x) = 7$

$12x - 6 + 3 - x = 7$

$11x - 3 = 7$

$11x = 7 + 3$

$11x = 10$

$$x = \frac{10}{11}$$

CHAPTER 5

1. $x = \frac{1}{2}$

$$x - \frac{x+1}{2} = 4x - (1 + 2x) - \frac{x}{2}$$

$$x - \frac{x+1}{2} = 4x - 1 - 2x - \frac{x}{2}$$

$$2\left(x - \frac{x+1}{2} = 4x - 1 - 2x - \frac{x}{2}\right)$$

$$2x - \frac{\cancel{2}(x+1)}{\cancel{2}} = 8x - 2 - 4x - \frac{\cancel{2}x}{\cancel{2}}$$

$2x - x - 1 = 3x - 2$
$x - 1 = 3x - 2$
$x - 3x = -2 + 1$
$-2x = -1$
$x = \frac{1}{2}$

2. $x = \frac{55}{4}$

$$10 - \frac{3x}{5} = x - 12$$

$$5\left(10 - \frac{3x}{5} = x - 12\right)$$

$$50 - \frac{\cancel{5}(3x)}{\cancel{5}} = 5x - 60$$

$50 - 3x = 5x - 60$
$50 + 60 = 5x + 3x$
$110 = 8x$

$$\frac{110}{8} = x$$

$$\frac{55}{4} = x$$

3. $x = 5$

$$2(x-2) = 5 + \frac{x-1}{4}$$

$$2x - 4 = 5 + \frac{x-1}{4}$$

$$4\left(2x - 4 = 5 + \frac{x-1}{4}\right)$$

$$8x - 16 = 20 + \frac{\cancel{4}(x-1)}{\cancel{4}}$$

$8x - 16 = 20 + x - 1$

$8x - 16 = 19 + x$

$8x - x = 19 + 16$

$7x = 35$

$$x = \frac{35}{7}$$

$x = 5$

4. $x = 2$

$$\frac{5}{x} = \frac{1}{2} + \frac{2 + x}{x}$$

$$x\left(\frac{5}{x} = \frac{1}{2} + \frac{2 + x}{x}\right)$$

$$2x\left(\frac{5}{x}\right) = 2x\left(\frac{1}{2}\right) + 2x\left(\frac{2 + x}{x}\right)$$

$$2\not{x}\left(\frac{5}{\not{x}}\right) = \not{2}x\left(\frac{1}{\not{2}}\right) + 2\not{x}\left(\frac{2 + x}{\not{x}}\right)$$

$$10 = x + 2(2 + x)$$

$10 = x + 4 + 2x$

$10 = 3x + 4$

$10 - 4 = 3x$

$6 = 3x$

$$\frac{6}{3} = x$$

$2 = x$

5. $5 = 5$

$$\frac{5}{x} = \frac{1}{2} + \frac{2 + x}{x}$$

$$\frac{5}{2} = \frac{1}{2} + \frac{2 + 2}{2}$$

$$\frac{5}{2} = \frac{1}{2} + \frac{4}{2}$$

$$2\left(\frac{5}{2} = \frac{1}{2} + \frac{4}{2}\right)$$

$$\cancel{2}\left(\frac{5}{\cancel{2}} = \frac{1}{\cancel{2}} + \frac{4}{\cancel{2}}\right)$$

$5 = 1 + 4$

$5 = 5$

6. $x = -7$

$$13 + \frac{3}{x} = 12 - \frac{4}{x}$$

$$x\left(13 + \frac{3}{x} = 12 - \frac{4}{x}\right)$$

$$13x + \frac{\cancel{x}(3)}{\cancel{x}} = 12x - \frac{\cancel{x}(4)}{\cancel{x}}$$

$13x + 3 = 12x - 4$

$13x - 12x = -4 - 3$

$x = -7$

7. $-88 = -88$

$$13 + \frac{3}{x} = 12 - \frac{4}{x}$$

$$13 + \frac{3}{-7} = 12 - \frac{4}{-7}$$

$$-7\left(13 + \frac{3}{-7} = 12 - \frac{4}{-7}\right)$$

$$-91 + \frac{\cancel{-7}(3)}{\cancel{-7}} = -84 - \frac{\cancel{-7}(4)}{\cancel{-7}}$$

$-91 + 3 = -84 - 4$

$-88 = -88$

8. $x = \frac{22}{3}$

$$\frac{8+3}{x} = \frac{5-2}{2}$$

$2(8 + 3) = x(5 - 2)$
$16 + 6 = 5x - 2x$
$22 = 3x$
$\frac{22}{3} = x$

9. $x = 135$

$$\frac{15}{8x} = \frac{2}{9+x}$$

$15(9 + x) = 2(8x)$
$135 + 15x = 16x$
$135 = 16x - 15x$
$135 = x$

10. $r = -\frac{22}{7}$

$$\frac{26}{8-r} = \frac{2}{4+r}$$

$26(4 + r) = 2(8 - r)$
$104 + 26r = 16 - 2r$
$104 - 16 = -2r - 26r$
$88 = -28r$

$-\frac{88}{28} = r$

$-\frac{22}{7} = r$

CHAPTER 6

1. $x = -\frac{7}{8}y$

   $13x + 4y = 5x - 3y$

   $13x - 5x = -3y - 4y$

   $8x = -7y$

   $x = -\frac{7}{8}y$

2. $n = 3$

   $6r + 4n = 12$ $(r = 0)$

   $6(0) + 4n = 12$

   $4n = 12$

   $n = \frac{12}{4}$

   $n = 3$

3. **(3, 0)**

   $3(3) + 2y = 9$

   $9 + 2y = 9$

   $2y = 9 - 9$

   $2y = 0$

   $y = 0$

4. **(–3, 9)**

   $3(-3) + 2y = 9$

   $-9 + 2y = 9$

   $2y = 9 + 9$

   $2y = 18$

   $y = \frac{18}{2}$

   $y = 9$

5. **(3, 0)**

$3x + 2(0) = 9$

$3x + 0 = 9$

$3x = 9$

$$x = \frac{9}{3}$$

$x = 3$

6. **(–5, 12)**

$3x + 2(12) = 9$

$3x + 24 = 9$

$3x = -15$

$$x = -\frac{15}{3}$$

$x = -5$

7. yes

$2x + 3y = 12$ (3, 2)

$2(3) + 3(2) = 12$

$6 + 6 = 12$

8. no

$y = 3x + 1$ (10, 3)

$3 = 3(10) + 1$

$3 = 30 + 1$

$3 \neq 31$

9. yes

$2a - 3b = 20$ (16, 4)

$2(16) - 3(4) = 20$

$32 - 12 = 20$

$20 = 20$

10. no

$8g - 3h = 8$ (3, 5)

$8(3) - 3(5) = 8$

$24 - 15 = 8$

$9 \neq 8$

CHAPTER 7

1. 89

$(3 \times 3 \times 3 \times 3) + (2 \times 2 \times 2)$

$3^4 + 2^3 = 89$

$81 + 8 = 89$

2. 7,221

$5^5 + 8^4 =$

$(5 \times 5 \times 5 \times 5 \times 5) + (8 \times 8 \times 8 \times 8) =$

$3{,}125 + 4{,}096 = 7{,}221$

3. $x = -4\frac{1}{6}$

$4(2x + 2^2) + 4x = 6x - 3^2$

$4(2x + 4) + 4x = 6x - 3^2$ Work within parentheses first.

$8x + 16 + 4x = 6x - 9$ Simplify any other exponents.

$8x + 4x - 6x = -9 - 16$

$6x = -25$

$x = -\frac{25}{6}$

$x = -4\frac{1}{6}$

4. 4.

$(8 + 3^3) + (4 - 5^4) = x + 20$

$8 + 27 + 4 - 625 = x + 20$

$-586 = x + 20$

$-586 - 20 = x$

$-606 = x$

5. 5.

$x(3^2 + 2^3) \Diamond 3x(5^2) = 50$

$x(9 + 8) \Diamond 3x(25) = 50$

$x(17) \Diamond 3x(25) = 50$

$17x \Diamond 75x = 50$

$1{,}275x^2 = 50$

$$x^2 = \frac{2}{51}$$

$$x = \sqrt{\frac{2}{51}}$$

6. 6.

$\sqrt{81} + \sqrt{169}$

$9 + 13 = 22$

7. 7.

$\sqrt{147}$

$\sqrt{49 \times 3}$

$\sqrt{49} \times \sqrt{3}$

$7\sqrt{3}$

8. 8.

$5\sqrt{12} - 13\sqrt{27} + 17\sqrt{45}$

$5\sqrt{4 \times 3} - 13\sqrt{9 \times 3} + 17\sqrt{9 \times 5}$ Simplify roots.

$5(2)\sqrt{3} - 13(3)\sqrt{3} + 17(3)\sqrt{5}$ Remove perfect squares.

$10\sqrt{3} - 39\sqrt{3} + 51\sqrt{5}$

$-29\sqrt{3} + 51\sqrt{5}$

9. 9.

$\sqrt{5}(2 - \sqrt{3})$

$2\sqrt{5} - \sqrt{15}$

10. 10.

$-2\sqrt{12} \times (-5\sqrt{3})$

$10\sqrt{36}$ Multiply coefficients and roots.

$10 \times 6 = 60$

CHAPTER 8

1. $4 \cdot 4^5 = 4^6$ can be solved with the multiplication law.
2. $(2^3)^2$ can be solved with the power of a power law.
3. $(5 \cdot 7)^3 = 5^3 \cdot 7^3$ can be solved with the power of a product law.
4. 5

   $5x^0$

   $5 \cdot 1 = 5$

5. x^{22}

   $x^2(x^4)^5$

   $x^2 \cdot x^{20} = x^{20+2} = x^{22}$

6. $256x^{10}$

   $(4x^2)^3(2x^2)^2$

   $4^3x^6 \cdot 2^2x^4$

   $64x^6 \cdot 4x^4$

   $256x^{10}$

7. 7.

   $(x^3y)(xy^2)$

   $x^{3+1} \cdot y^{1+2}$

   x^4y^3

8. $\frac{16}{729}$

$\left(\frac{2^2}{3^3}\right)^2$

$\frac{2^{2 \cdot 2}}{3^{3 \cdot 2}} = \frac{2^4}{3^6} = \frac{16}{729}$

9. 25

$\frac{5^4}{5^2}$

$5^{4-2} = 5^2 = 25$

10. $\frac{4y^2}{9x^4}$

$\frac{(2xy)^2}{(3x^2)^3}$

$\frac{2^2x^2y^2}{3^3x^6} = \frac{4x^2y^2}{9x^6} = \frac{4y^2}{9x^4}$

CHAPTER 9

1. $6x^2 + 56x + 18$

$(6x + 2)(x + 9)$

First $6x \cdot x =$ **6x2**

Outer $6x \cdot 9 =$ **54x**

Inner $2 \cdot x =$ **2x**

Last $2 \cdot 9 =$ **18**

$6x^2 + 54x + 2x + 18$

$6x^2 + 56x + 18$

2. $4x^2 - x - 3$

$(4x + 3)(x - 1)$

First $4x \cdot x =$ **$4x2$**

Outer $4x \cdot (-1) =$ **$-4x$**

Inner $3 \cdot x =$ **$3x$**

Last $3 \cdot (-1) =$ **-3**

$4x^2 - 4x + 3x - 3$

$4x^2 - x - 3$

3. $15b^2 - b - 6$

$(5b + 3)(3b - 2)$

First $5b \cdot 3b =$ **$15b2$**

Outer $5b \cdot (-2) =$ **$-10b$**

Inner $3 \cdot 3b =$ **$9b$**

Last $3 \cdot (-2) =$ **-6**

$15b^2 - 10b + 9b - 6$

$15b^2 - b - 6$

4. $36z^2 - 16$

$(6z - 4)(6z + 4)$

First $6z \cdot 6z =$ **$36z2$**

Outer $6z \cdot 4 =$ **$24z$**

Inner $-4 \cdot 6z =$ **$-24z$**

Last $-4 \cdot 4 =$ **-16**

$36z^2 + 24z - 24z - 16$

$36z^2 - 16$

5. $36x^2y^2 + 78xy - 14$

$(12xy - 2)(3xy + 7)$

First $12xy \cdot 3xy =$ **$36x2y2$**

Outer $12xy \cdot 7 =$ **$84xy$**

Inner $-2 \cdot 3xy =$ **$-6xy$**

Last $-2 \cdot 7 =$ **-14**

$36x^2y^2 + 84xy - 6xy - 14$

$36x^2y^2 + 78xy - 14$

6. $25y^2 + 70y + 49$
$(5y + 7)^2$
To square a binomial, use the formula
$(a - b)^2 = a^2 - 2ab + b^2$
$(5y)^2 + 2(5y)(7) + 7^2$
$25y^2 + 70y + 49$

7. $64z^2 - 80z + 25$
$(8z - 5)^2$
To square a binomial, use the formula
$(a - b)^2 = a^2 - 2ab + b^2$
$(8z)^2 - 2(8z)(5) + (5)^2$
$64z^2 - 80z + 25$

8. $x^3 - 2x^2 - x + 2$
$(x + 1)(x^2 - 3x + 2)$
$x^3 - 3x^2 + 2x + x^2 - 3x + 2$
$x^3 - 2x^2 - x + 2$

9. $6x^3 + 7x^2 - 3x - 1$
$(3x^2 + 5x + 1)(2x - 1)$
To make distributing easier, rewrite as
$(2x - 1)(3x^2 + 5x + 1)$
$6x^3 + 10x^2 + 2x - 3x^2 - 5x - 1$
$6x^3 + 7x^2 - 3x - 1$

10. $3y^3 + y^2 - 2y - 2$
$(y - 1)(3y^2 + 4y + 2)$
$3y^3 + 4y^2 + 2y - 3y^2 - 4y - 2$
$3y^3 + y^2 - 2y - 2$

CHAPTER 10

1. If n is the first number, then the second number would be $\frac{4}{5}n$.

You can put any numbers in for n. For example if $n = 5$, you could find

the second number by writing $\frac{4}{5} \times 5 = 4$.

Original question: One number is $\frac{4}{5}$ of another.

2. Let x equal Sara's age. If Margo is three times older than Sara, Margo's age is $3x$.
   Original question: Margo is three times older than Sara.

3. Let m equal the number of quarters Mike has. That means Jeff has $8m$ quarters. For example, if Mike has 2 quarters, Jeff has 16. If Mike has 5 quarters, Jeff has 40.
   Original question: Jeff has eight times as many quarters as Mike.

4. If we call the first number n, then the next consecutive integer would be $n + 1$. So, if the first integer is 10, the second is $10 + 1$, or 11.
   Original question: Two numbers are consecutive integers.

5. If l is the length of the rectangle, the width is $7 + 3l$. So, if 10 is the length, the width is $7 + 3(10)$, or 37.
   Original question: The width of a rectangle is seven more than three times its length.

6. Let n equal "a number." Then, another number is $5n - 9$. So, if one number is 2, the other is $5(2) - 9$, or 1.
   Original question: Five times a number decreased by nine is equal to another number.

7. Let n equal the smaller integer. Then, $n + 1$ is the next consecutive integer.
   $n + (n + 1) = 39$
   $2n + 1 = 39$
   $2n = 39 - 1$
   $2n = 38$
   $n = \frac{38}{2}$

$n = 19, n + 1 = 20$

Original question: The sum of two consecutive integers is 39. Find the integers.

8. Let n = the number.

$3n - 9 = 3 + 2n$

$3n - 2n = 3 + 9$

$n = 12$

Check the answer:

$3(12) - 9 = 3 + 2(12)$

$36 - 9 = 3 + 24$

$27 = 27$

It checks out.

Original question: Nine less than three times a number is equal to three more than twice the number. Find the number.

9. Let k = Kate's age. Let $6k$ = Laura's age.

$k + 6k = 28$

$7k = 28$

$$k = \frac{28}{7}$$

$k = 4$

Since $6k$ = Laura's age, Laura's age = 6(4) = 24.

Check the answer:

$4 + 6(4) = 28$

$4 + 24 = 28$

$28 = 28$

Original question: Laura is six times older than Kate. The sum of their ages is 28. How old are Laura and Kate?

10. Let n be the smallest of the consecutive integers.

Then, $n + 1$ = the middle integer, and $n + 2$ = the largest integer.

$$n + (n + 1) - 11 = n + 2$$
$$2n + 1 - 11 = n + 2$$
$$2n - 10 = n + 2$$
$$2n - n = 2 + 10$$
$$n = 12$$

If the smallest integer is 12, the middle one is 13, and the largest is 14.

Original question: Find three consecutive integers such that the sum of the first two decreased by 11 is equal to the third.

CHAPTER 11

1. Quadrant II
2. Quadrant I
3. Quadrant IV
4. Quadrant III

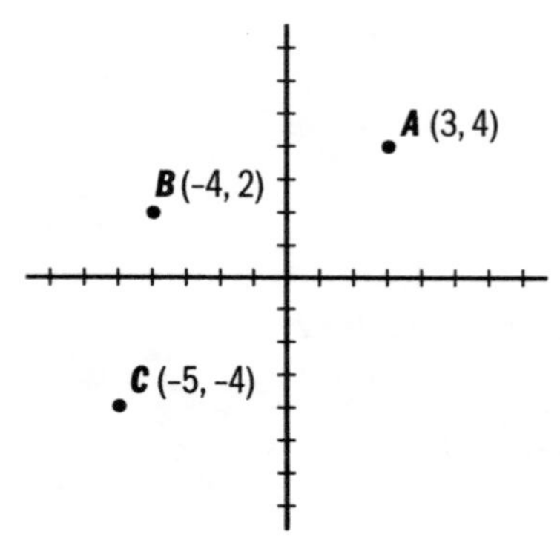

5. *A* (3, 4)
6. *B* (-4, 2)
7. *C* (-5, -4)
8. (-5, 4)
9. (0, -3)
10. $\left(\frac{1}{2}, -2\right)$

CHAPTER 12

1. (4, -5)

   $5x + 2y = 10$

   $5(4) + 2y = 10$

   $20 + 2y = 10$

   $2y = 10 - 20$

   $2y = -10$

   $$y = -\frac{10}{2}$$

   $y = -5$

   The ordered pair is (4, -5).

2. (-2, 10)

   $5x + 2y = 10$

   $5(-2) + 2y = 10$

   $-10 + 2y = 10$

   $2y = 10 + 10$

   $2y = 20$

   $$y = \frac{20}{2}$$

   $y = 10$

   The ordered pair is (-2, 10).

3. (2, 0)

   $5x + 2y = 10$

   $5x + 2(0) = 10$

   $5x + 0 = 10$

   $5x = 10$

   $$x = \frac{10}{5}$$

   $x = 2$

   The ordered pair is (2, 0).

4. $10 = 10$
   $5x + 2y = 10$
   $5(4) + 2(-5) = 10$
   $20 - 10 = 10$
   $10 = 10$

5. $10 = 10$
   $5x + 2y = 10$
   $5(-2) + 2(10) = 10$
   $-10 + 20 = 10$
   $10 = 10$

6. $10 = 10$
   $5x + 2y = 10$
   $5(2) + 2(0) = 10$
   $10 + 0 = 10$
   $10 = 10$

7.

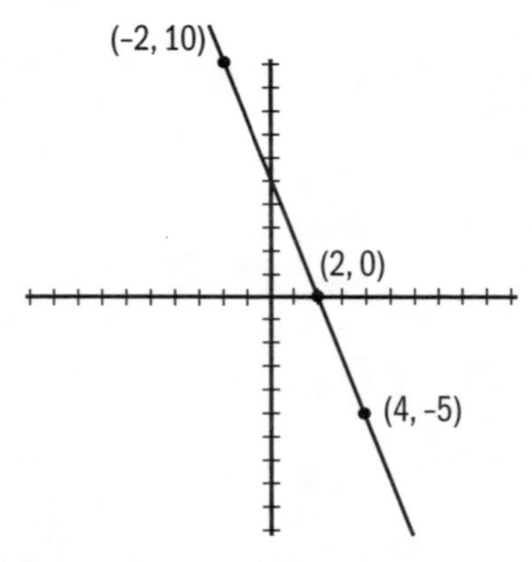

8. The y-intercept is 5.
9. The x-intercept is 2.

10. No. The coordinates don't make the original equation true:

$5x + 2y = 10$

$5(4) + 2(5) \neq 10$

$20 + 10 \neq 10$

$30 \neq 10$

CHAPTER 13

1. 36

$|-22| + |14|$

$22 + 14 = 36$

2. $8x - 16$

$2\{x - 3[4 - (x + 1)] + 1\}$

$2\{x - 3[4 - x - 1] + 1\}$

$2\{x - 3[3 - x] + 1\}$

$2\{x - 9 + 3x + 1\}$

$2\{4x - 8\}$

$8x - 16$

3. $\frac{2}{17}$

$(14n + 3n) + 2(5 + n) = 12 + 2n$

$14n + 3n + 10 + 2n = 12 + 2n$

$19n + 10 = 12 + 2n$

$19n - 2n = 12 - 10$

$17n = 2$

$$n = \frac{2}{17}$$

4. $3 + 12x$

$$\frac{4 + 3x}{2} + 2x + \frac{5x - 1}{2}$$

$$2\left(\frac{4 + 3x}{2} + 2x + \frac{5x - 1}{2}\right)$$

$$\frac{\not{2}(4 + 3x)}{\not{2}} + 4x + \frac{\not{2}(5x - 1)}{\not{2}}$$

$4 + 3x + 4x + 5x - 1$

$3 + 12x$

5. $y = 1\frac{2}{7}$

$4x + 14y = 12x + 2$

$4(2) + 14y = 12(2) + 2$

$8 + 14y = 24 + 2$

$14y = 24 + 2 - 8$

$14y = 18$

$$y = \frac{18}{14}$$

$$y = 1\frac{2}{7}$$

6. $x = -21$

$3(2x + 2^2) = 5x - 3^2$

$3(2x + 4) = 5x - 9$

$6x + 12 = 5x - 9$

$6x - 5x = -9 - 12$

$x = -21$

7. $3^{14} = 4,782,969$

$3^2(3^3)^4$

$3^2 \cdot 3^{12} = 3^{2+12} = 3^{14}$

$3^{14} = 4,782,969$

8. $6x^2 + 40x - 14$

$(6x - 2)(x + 7)$

$6x^2 + 42x - 2x - 14$

$6x^2 + 40x - 14$

9. 14, 15, 16

n = the first number

$n + 1$ = the second number

$n + 2$ = the third number

$n + (n + 1) + (n + 2) = 45$

$3n + 3 = 45$

$3n = 45 - 3$

$3n = 42$

$$n = \frac{42}{3}$$

$n = 14$

$14 + 15 + 16 = 45$

10. $y = 2$

$3x + 4y = 14$ (2, ?)

$3(2) + 4y = 14$

$6 + 4y = 14$

$4y = 14 - 6$

$4y = 8$

$$y = \frac{8}{4}$$

$y = 2$